Eyfroth

OF Lindisfarne

(NOT A SAINT!)

Kate
Tristram

This first edition published by:
Lindisfarne Scriptorium Limited,
Farne House, Marygate,
Holy Island of Lindisfarne,
TD15 2SJ, United Kingdom.

ISBN-13: 978 1 909041 25 7

10 9 8 7 6 5 4 3 2 1

British Library Cataloguing in Publication Data. A catalogue record for this book is available from the British Library.

Typeset and produced by Lindisfarne Scriptorium Limited.
Printed and bound in England.

Contact. www.lindisfarne-scriptorium.co.uk
        enquiry@lindisfarne-scriptorium.co.uk

EGFROTH OF LINDISFARNE – NOT A SAINT
BY KATE TRISTRAM

PREFACE

CHAPTER 1   BEGINNINGS

CHAPTER 2   IN THE SCHOOL

CHAPTER 3   GROWING UP

CHAPTER 4   DECISIONS

CHAPTER 5   DEATH OF A FOUNDER AND OTHERS

CHAPTER 6   UNDER BISHOP FINAN

CHAPTER 7   CONFLICT

CHAPTER 8   CUTHBERT AS PRIOR

CHAPTER 9   CUTHBERT AS HERMIT AND BISHOP

CHAPTER 10   ELEVATION

CHAPTER 11   LAST WORDS

EPILOGUE BY BROTHER JOHN

Preface

Egfroth is an invented character. (His name appears in that great work of history *1066 and all that*, in the form Eggfroth; but our Egfroth preferred to spell it with a single g, as that seemed to him more dignified.)

Many of the other characters in the book are real people. The major events are real events. I have invented details about Egfroth, but where I have dealt with real events I have tried to get my facts right and where I have dealt with real people I have tried to be true to the sources.

Through Egfroth I tell the story of the 7th century in Northumbria, as it might have appeared to an ordinary monk of Lindisfarne. Egfroth is ordinary. He solves no mysteries and creates no work of art. He follows the lead of others. He enters the monastic school on Lindisfarne as a child of ten, two years after Aidan founded the monastery. He dies as an old man of seventy two (old for that period) a year after the 'elevation' of Saint Cuthbert's body. He lives through this most fascinating age of Northumbrian history, and he sets eyes on all the stars in the galaxy of saints.

Egfroth is English (Anglo-Saxon). His great-grandfather came in one of the early parties of Anglo-Saxon raiders and infiltrators into North Northumbria, and married a British girl before settling down to a life of fishing and farming. His family are free peasants, reasonably prosperous.

So Egfroth is not 'Celtic' and would not have understood that word. All the same he was trained in an Irish monastery, as Lindisfarne was for its first thirty years. He is not the kind of person who can put his faith clearly into words. Yet he has learnt it by living alongside some extremely good men, to whom their faith was everything. He expresses his faith by his loyalty to what he has been taught, and he seeks to serve God and others within the monastery.

If he had lived in the days of paper he might have written his reminiscences, but I could not provide him with enough parchment: it was too expensive. So this book takes the form of recollections in old age, told to a fascinated young monk who has only just joined the monastery after experiencing a cure from what appeared to be epilepsy, a healing which took place at Saint Cuthbert's tomb. I have called this young man Brother John, and at the time of these conversations he is nineteen years old.

Now read on and let Egfroth tell his story…

Chapter 1   Beginnings

Let's sit here up on the Heugh for a while, Brother John, and look around on the Island and down on the place where it all started. As I told you, I was 10 years old when I entered the monastery and was the youngest boy in the school. Now I am 72 and am the oldest of the brothers here. 62 years… and you have said you would like to hear all about it. You're a kind lad! Old men like to talk about the past and, although everyone is good to me here, the friends of my earlier days are all dead. But my memory is good, thank God, though the rest of me is shaky. So I will tell you all I can.

I remember so clearly how it all began for me: the day my life changed for ever. I was 10 years old and I had just rushed out of our cottage in a rage. My mother had said, "Oh, Egfroth! Do go somewhere else for a bit and find something to do!" I felt persecuted. Yes, I was always dropping things, and not listening, and so on. My mother was always telling me how clever my two older brothers and two older sisters were. You would think *they* always got everything right. So I felt stupid.

Anyhow, on this particular day out I went and I was stamping along the lane when I saw our Irish bishop, Aidan, coming to meet me with two monks of Lindisfarne. I didn't expect them to notice a small boy so I stood respectfully to one side to let them pass. But I have since learned that Aidan noticed everybody, man, woman, or child. He looked at me and smiled and said, "Surely I've seen you before?"

"Yes, father," I answered; "I'm Egfroth. You baptised me and the rest of my family last year."

"That's good," he said. Then he looked at my red and angry face. "But now you're in trouble?" So I told him, ending, "They're not cruel to me, really they're not. It's just that they worry about whether I'll ever be able to do a job, or get anything right."

He was silent for a moment as if he were thinking, or almost as if he were listening. Then he said, "Would you like to come and work with me in the monastery?" I was completely astonished.

4

I said "What, be a monk?" Then he laughed. "We wouldn't make you a monk just yet," he said. "But we have all kinds of work. There's cooking and cleaning and farming and fishing and praying and singing and reading and writing… Think about it. I'll come and talk to your parents in a day or two."

So a day or two later he came to our house. He told my family what I would be doing and he told them they could come and see me as often as they liked. At first they just didn't know what to make of it. I think if I had been the eldest son or even very useful, they mightn't have let me go. In the end my father turned to me. Boys of 10 aren't usually consulted about their future, but he said, "What do you think about it?" I said, "I'd like to go and try." So it was decided.

I was very excited on the day. My home wasn't far from the Island, just up the coast. We might have travelled by boat, but both my brothers were out in our craft, fishing. So my father, who was coming with me, said we would walk. As I said good-bye my mother was suddenly quite tearful. "Don't forget," she said, "that you've always got a home here." Even my sisters stopped teasing me that morning.

We set out and walked mostly in silence to the monastery. My father was never a man to talk a lot. When we got there Aidan met us briefly and then left us alone to say good-bye. My father put his arm round my shoulders, gave me a hug, and said, "Be a good lad." I watched him walk back across the sands. I suddenly felt quite empty.

But when I turned round there was a boy, a bit older than me, standing there. He gave me a friendly grin and said, "Hello. I'm Chad. Come on; I'll show you round." So he showed me where we ate and where we slept. I was to share a hut with him; it was basic but comfortable enough and I wasn't used to luxury. He showed me where we washed, but I was pleased to hear that the boys were allowed to swim in the sea quite often; that was the only kind of washing I enjoyed in those days! He took me to a meal and into the church, though I didn't of course understand a word of what was said there.

5

Then it was nearly bedtime, and suddenly Chad wasn't there. I was wondering what to do when he came back, and this time with him was Aidan himself. Aidan was carrying in his arms a tiny kitten: whitish-grey, with a white mouth, white underside, white paws and a white tip to its tail. Chad was grinning in the background, but it was not to him but to me that Aidan said, "I've brought you another friend and I've brought you your first job. This is Pangur. You are now the monastery's cat-minder. Look after him well. This cat will grow up to be important to us and so will you."

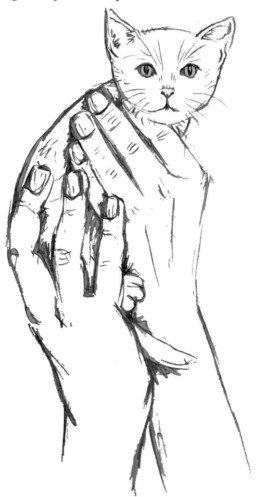

Brother John, that night I went to bed happy.

I hadn't been long in the monastery, brother, before I discovered that I was not useless. As well as being quite a hit with the cat – for Pangur and I loved each other from the start – I actually had other gifts I could offer to the life.

First, I had a good singing voice, clear and high. Of course when I was at home with my family I knew I liked to sing. But they didn't always appreciate it very much. In fact my singing often used to irritate my mother, when she was trying to concentrate and I wasn't, or when she thought it was a sign that I didn't care. I was astonished, when the monks heard me singing, that they liked my voice so much. It was amazing! I worked very hard at learning the psalms and the chants and, it seemed for the first time in my life, I was praised.

Secondly, I was big and strong for my age and all the time growing bigger and stronger. So I was often useful in pulling and pushing and digging and hauling. I quite enjoyed doing that as long as I knew what they wanted and didn't have to make any decisions. I've never really liked making decisions! Later in life my size and strength gave me some interesting experiences, as I'll tell you. But as a boy I sometimes found it a problem. I was a clumsy child and an ungainly youth. Much of the time I really didn't know where my hands and feet were! Some of the monks thought I was older than I was and expected too much of me. They thought me lazy, when in fact some of the time I was just tired and some of the time I was just hungry. Times of fasting could be hard, though I must say that Aidan was good to growing boys and didn't expect them to be very austere. Yes, looking back on it all now, I must say that the monks in general were kind.

The third gift I had to offer was that I had had a grandfather. You may say, so had we all – two, in fact. But it didn't seem to be so for all the boys. I never quite liked to ask Chad and his three brothers about their family. As far as I know no-one ever came to visit them, and they never mentioned anyone. I've got a feeling that they might have been orphans. But I had known one of my grandfathers, my father's father, who lived not far from us. He felt sorry for me because I was the youngest, and because my family thought I was stupid. So he spent quite a lot of time with me, telling me stories. He was a marvellous storyteller, the best I have ever known. But when I got here I found that some of the boys didn't know these stories. I had a little of my grandfather's gift. So when we boys had time to ourselves I used to tell them what my grandfather had told me, and I found that I and my stories were quite popular.

You ask, what kind of stories? Most of them were about kings and battles. My grandfather was lame in one leg: he was wounded fighting for King Aethelfrith. Aethelfrith was his great hero, though he quite admired King Edwin as well. These two kings were mortal enemies, though that didn't bother my grandfather. Kings and nobles lived for fighting, he said, so of course sometimes they got killed. But so what? Death in battle was the best way to die and the quickest way to the warrior's 'heaven'. My grandfather was a pagan and he thought of heaven as a continuation of the warrior's life of courage and prowess and success. He did not hold it against Edwin that he had been involved in the death of Aethelfrith.

One of the stories he told me was about this island, before Aethelfrith became king. Before we English came and called the island Lindisfarne the people round here were British and this island had a British name, Medcaut. When we English came into these northern parts, looking for lands to conquer, we first captured the bit along the coast, including the rock of Bamburgh. At that point the British woke up. They weren't going to sit still and let the English take their land. So four British kings sent armies to meet together and throw the English back into the sea. They might have done it too, as they were stronger than our ancestors at that time. They even got some English leaders penned in on the island of Medcaut. But then, tragedy. It seems that their greatest warrior, a Briton called Urien, somehow aroused the jealousy of the other British leaders. One dark night he was treacherously killed, by an unknown hand, but a British one. The British forces then lost heart and melted away, and what might have been called 'the battle of Medcaut' never happened. My grandfather always ended this story a little sadly. I think he would have liked a good battle.

But he told it with some sympathy for the British. After all, he was half-British himself. (Did I forget to tell you that my great-grandfather had married a British girl?) Yet there was another battle story involving the British, which my grandfather told without a trace of sympathy for them. King Aethelfrith had gone down to fight in the area around Chester, and found himself faced not only with an army of British soldiers but also with an 'army' of British Christian monks who had come out to pray against him. These monks were of course unarmed. But it seems that Aethelfrith was a religious pagan, as my grandfather certainly was. They both took it for granted that prayers were real weapons and really might make things happen. So people who prayed against them were real enemies, to be taken seriously and disposed of. Aethelfrith calmly massacred the monks.

As boys we argued a lot about that story, Brother John. Some of us were frightened by it and imagined ourselves, as unarmed monks, being attacked. Others said no, Aethelfrith was right: if we were going to be Christian monks we must believe at least as strongly as the pagans do, that prayer is important and causes things to happen. One or two of us were interested in the fact that Aethelfrith was killed very soon after he fought that battle. Was it a kind of judgment on him? My grandfather didn't think so. He thought Aethelfrith died an appropriate and admirable death.

I asked him once about the battle in which he had been wounded. He said it had been a long way from here, over to the west. It was fought at the place called Degsa's Stone, and the enemy was an Irish king who had invaded. He told me that a lot of men were killed there, particularly a lot of Irish, and it was a great victory for Aethelfrith. I don't think he wanted to give me all the gory details, since I was only about 8 years old, but he did tell me that he didn't think the Irish would care to attack the English again. He himself had been wounded in the leg, and had had difficulty in getting home. The wound had never healed properly but that, he said, had not stopped him living.

My grandfather had admiration for King Edwin as well as King Aethelfrith, though of course as Edwin made his main centre at

York not so much of him was seen up here. Sometimes, however, he came to his place at Ad Gefrin: it's just under the mountain over there, John; you can almost see it from here. My grandfather had certainly set eyes on him. He said that Edwin was a good fighter and also a good ruler in peacetime. When Edwin was killed in battle my grandfather lived to see the return of Aethelfrith's son Oswald, and the royal centre again established at Bamburgh. He found that very exciting, but he died soon after Oswald became king.

So these were the stories, John, which I used to tell my young classmates, though no doubt with a lot of invented detail and suitable sound effects! I still think that although most of us became monks we needed to know these things. Some of them became great missionaries and dealt with kings: they needed to know how a military society thought. And all of us needed to know something of the history of our own people. Anyway, they were good stories. Pangur became quite an expert in them when I had no-one else to talk to, but he liked them too!

One day, during a pause in our usual work we were sitting in a group talking of kings and battles as boys do, even boys in a monastery. Particularly we were talking about King Oswald. We knew he was a friend of Aidan, and he had visited our monastery a few days before. We hadn't expected to see him except from a distance, but to our delight he came into the school and had a word with each of us. Most of us had never spoken to a real king! He was handsome too, and he and his attendants looked so bright in their coloured clothes and gold ornaments. Our clothes were warm and serviceable but very plain. So afterwards we couldn't stop talking about it.

We knew of course that Oswald had been in exile as a boy and had been taught the Christian faith by the monks of Iona. That made a link with us. We knew that when King Edwin was killed Oswald brought a small army into Northumbria, fought and won the battle of Heavenfield and became king. We didn't know much more. But then one of the Irish monks happened to walk past us as we were talking, and heard the name 'Oswald', so he stopped and said, "Have you heard how Saint Columba helped King Oswald to win that battle?"

"No," we chorused. "Tell us."

So he sat down for a moment with us.

"Your King Oswald himself tells this story," he said, "so of course it must be true! One night, as he was getting ready to fight the battle of Heavenfield, while he was asleep in his tent he had a dream – or a vision. Saint Columba, who had been dead for about 40 years, appeared to him, looking so huge and shining that he seemed to fill all the camp. He told Oswald who he was, and said he was on his side. He promised that God would give Oswald victory in battle and that he would become king. When Oswald woke up and told his soldiers about this vision everyone felt ten times bigger and stronger. So they were inspired to win the battle against a much bigger army. Of course you know that Oswald was already a Christian and he had vowed to bring the Christian faith to the English. But it was this victory which made that possible, so he was able to invite us to come here from Iona. Your king himself told this story to our abbot back in our monastery there."

We were all thrilled by this. We hadn't heard it before. Of course we knew that Columba founded Iona but this connection with Oswald made him seem much nearer to us. So one of the boys said, "Tell us more about Saint Columba. What was he really like?" "Well," said the monk with the smile, "I didn't actually know him. As I said, he died about 40 years ago and I'm 35. But Iona was full of stories about him. Yes, I'll be glad to tell you. I can't stop any longer just now, but I'll get permission and we'll make a time together to talk about him." And so we did.

"The monastery at Iona," he said, "is very much like this one, since this one was modelled on it. As places I wouldn't say that the two islands are very much alike. But Columba didn't go to Iona until he was over forty. Before that he lived in Ireland. His family were very aristocratic – royal, really – and very powerful. I suppose Columba might have been a great king if he hadn't decided to become a monk. He was a keen Christian and became a monk early and founded many monasteries in Ireland."

"Then he decided to leave. There's some mystery about this decision. Columba didn't talk very much to his friends about it. Some monks said he was simply drawn, for the love of God, to leave everything and go out into the unknown. Some said he wanted to obey the Gospel's call to mission and go to the Picts. Some said there were darker reasons: that he had committed some sin and left home as a penance. I just don't know. Anyway, he left Ireland with a group of twelve men, just as Aidan came here with twelve of us. Eventually he got to Iona, found it was right for what he wanted, and stayed and built the monastery. Not that he stayed there forever. He spent a lot of time travelling, especially among the Picts, most of whom were not yet Christians, and he also went back to Ireland to visit his monasteries there. He lived about thirty years after he founded Iona, and died there as an old man in his middle seventies."

"What was he like as a person? He was a very tall man, strong; very clever; very handsome; with a particularly clear, ringing voice. He was a born leader and had all the confidence of a man of his class. He could be terrifying when he was angry, but he could also be very gentle."

"As well as all this he was a person of strange gifts, and many of the stories were about those. There are people who really do have powers which we know are real, and yet we can't explain them. Columba sometimes had the gift of knowing what was going to happen to people in the future and sometimes he knew things which were happening at that moment but a long way away. It was a bit eerie! It made people afraid of him, as people are when they can't explain something. Yet we believe that God gave him these gifts and he certainly used them for good, not evil. We were told he saved people's lives by warning them of dangers to come, such as storms at sea. He just knew whether the people who came to talk to him were genuine or not, and he was severe with those who were not. Sometimes he even prophesied when they would die, and gave the time and place, and they did die exactly as he said, though it wasn't his prophecies but other things which killed them."

Brother John, I really became quite scared with all this. I was glad it was Aidan who came here, not Columba. I know I'd have been terrified of Columba, the stories were gripping and we urged the monk to go on. I think he realized some of us younger ones were uneasy, so he changed his tone a little.

"Columba was always gentle to people in real need, often more gentle than other folk. For instance, he visited one monastery where the monks received him with great ceremony. There was a boy there who was a bit of a nuisance. Nobody thought well of him and he was expected to keep right out of the way. This boy was determined to see and if possible touch Columba. I think he had just been learning in the Gospels about the woman who touched Jesus' cloak. So, without anyone noticing, he crept right up behind Columba. But Columba knew. As I said, he was a big, strong man, and he suddenly put his hand behind him, grabbed the child and brought him to the front. The monks turned on the lad furiously, but Columba blessed him and prophesied he would have a great future. And so it turned out."

John, I liked that story. I remember the day I first heard it I had been in a lot of trouble. I'd been helping in the kitchen and everything had gone wrong. I had knocked over the milk bucket and dropped the basket of eggs, and felt that no-one loved me. But when I heard that story I began to dream. Perhaps I had a great future too…

Our story teller continued, "Columba was gentle to poor people, to women and to animals… I mean *some* animals. Once he knew by his gift of foresight that an exhausted heron would land on Iona, and he gave special instructions that it was to be treated like an honoured guest for three days, then it would recover its strength and find its way back to Ireland. But some animals were a threat. Once, when he was up in Pictland, by a river called River Ness, he was told of a great water beast that attacked people. However, Columba wanted a boat brought over from the other side so he ordered a monk to swim over and get it. The obedient monk swam. Then the monster appeared, showing all its teeth, and went for the monk. Columba just yelled at it (you remember I said he had a good voice) and the great beast turned and fled."

13

We liked these stories, John, and our monk told them in much greater detail than I can remember. Though I was quite glad that Columba was not on Lindisfarne, I would have liked to have gone to Iona, but never had the chance. Of course we ceased to be directly under Iona after King Oswiu's Synod, as I'll explain later, but I'm glad we are still in friendly contact. Our present King Aldfrith spent many years on Iona before he became king and since then I know that Abbot Adomnan of Iona has visited him at least twice. It's good we still have the connection and I'm hopeful that Saint Columba in heaven keeps a friendly eye on Lindisfarne.

CHAPTER 2   IN THE SCHOOL

In the school we learned reading, writing and Latin. Of course when I started I had never seen a book, and just getting the idea of reading and writing was quite hard at first. Hard, but fascinating. Just the idea that I could make a particular mark on our wax tablets, or even in the sand, and other people might know what I meant, was quite a mystery; it was even more wonderful that I could know what they meant. Our teachers were kind; they made a game of it at first for us young beginners, but the words had to be all in Latin, because nobody wrote in anything else. I think that I was quite grown-up before I realized that if it was possible to write in Latin it would be possible to write in English, but nobody did.

Of course we learned Latin in many different ways. Since we were at different stages at the beginning we had individual help to recognize the letters, then to write the letters and so to make words. We were encouraged to learn the Latin names for the things we saw about us and to use them to one another. When we began to write words we copied verses from the psalms. The psalms were immensely important to our Irish teachers; we heard them sung in the church and so we remembered bits before we really began to understand the language. Our teachers gradually explained the meaning of the psalms we used most often. Amazingly our monks could actually speak Latin, as well as Irish and English. I wasn't very quick at all, brother, but, bit by bit, the written page took on meaning and I realized that I was actually reading.

The learning by heart never stopped. First we learned all the psalms, then we had also to learn the Gospels. Our teachers had enormous reverence for Jesus. We knew that we learned the Gospels so that always, to the end of our lives, we might live in our minds with our Lord and grow in obedience and indeed a kind of fellowship with him. We knew that the Christian life involved loving and following Jesus. Also, if we were to be missionaries we must carry in our heads the Gospel we were to give to others.

What you learn young tends to stick, brother, and to this day I know the psalms and the Gospels by heart, and in Latin too. The really bright pupils went on to other parts of the Bible, but that was about my limit. Yet it has done for me what they promised. One day I asked one of the teachers what all this was supposed to give us. "Light," he said, "light enough to live by and light enough to die by." Well, yes. As the years have passed I have found plenty of food for thought in what I have learned and plenty of guidance and help. I am thankful to have been a Christian and to have lived by that particular light.

But school wasn't just reading and writing and learning. Often our teachers would get us together in a group to talk about the Christian faith and life, the Bible and the whole world in which we live. I found those lessons have really stayed in my memory. You will have learned in a different way, since you didn't come into the monastery as a child.

"You remember," our teacher said, "that in our Creed we say that we believe in one God who made everything, heaven and earth, everything visible and invisible. There is nothing at all, from the biggest mountain to the tiniest insect that God did not make. You will never meet anything at all, in your whole life, that God did not make."

At that time I liked asking what I thought were awkward questions. So I said, "Did God make the demons and the powers of evil?"

"Yes," he said, "God made them but he did not make them evil. God made them good. They were angels when he first made them. But you know how we humans have it in our power to be good or bad? We can choose, and so can the angels. Some of them, a long while ago, chose to be bad and to defy God. So after that they couldn't any longer live in heaven. Now they live down here with us and they go on trying to spoil God's creation. Especially they try to make people wicked. But, my sons, there is no need to be afraid of them. They can't make you wicked unless you turn away from God. God has defeated them; Jesus won the victory on the cross; one day God will show them, and us, that he is really God. And that will be an end of their wickedness."

I wanted to change the subject. I didn't like all this talk about wickedness, so I said, "What are the demons actually made of?"

16

"Air," our teacher replied. "We think they are made of air. That is why you can't see them unless they make themselves visible in some shape or other, which they do sometimes. But that was a good question, and brings me nicely to the next thing I wanted to say. Everything that God made is made out of one or more of four basic materials. We call these the four elements: they are fire, air, water and earth. If we put these four elements in order of weight, the heaviest first, the order is earth, water, air and fire. Think about ordinary experience. When you light a fire, doesn't the flame always go upwards? That shows that fire is lighter than air. If you put anything containing air into water doesn't the air come to the top in bubbles? Air is lighter than water. But if you pour water out of a jar, doesn't the water always go downwards? Water is heavier than air. And if you put anything made of earth into water that thing sinks to the bottom. That's because earth is heavier than water."

I opened my mouth to say that, in my garden at home, if you put water on earth it's the water that sinks to the bottom. But I didn't say it. I shut up. I got the general idea.

So after school I went and told the whole thing to Pangur "I think you are made of earth, Pangur," I said. Just to prove me wrong he then leapt straight up on to the top of a nearby wall. That ought to have shown that he was lighter than air and so must be made of fire. Then I remembered that the teacher had said that humans are made of all four elements, and Pangur is nearly human. So?

Education is sometimes very puzzling.

In another lesson, Brother John, we were talking about the earth, the sun, the moon and the stars.

"What shape is the earth?" One boy asked.

That struck me as funny question, since you can see with your own eyes that it is flattish and lumpy. But it emerged that there was more to it than that.

"We don't know for sure," said our teacher. We think that the sun and the moon are round like balls, but there have been people who think they are flat like plates. I can't answer that question. But it is more important to know what they are for. God made them for us. We have a special name for the sun and the moon. We call them 'the luminaries' because they were made to give us light: the sun by day and the moon by night. They also divide up the year for us: not only winter and summer, or full moon and new moon, which is obvious, but they also help us to make a calendar so that we know when our particular feast days are, especially Easter."

At this point he went into an explanation about how to calculate the date of Easter. Chad sat there looking intelligent, but I'm afraid I went to sleep. Not even later in life did I quite manage to understand the whole business about the date of Easter.

When I woke up the master was talking about the stars. "We don't really know why God made the stars. We've never felt that they were particularly important to us, though we can understand that they might be for others: for example, for people who live in warmer, clearer climates, or for sailors finding their way across the sea. But there is a use we can make of them. You remember the psalmist sang of 'the moon and the stars which you have set in order'? We can look up at the stars and let them speak to us of the majesty of God, and very especially of the orderliness that he has given to his whole creation. We human beings, my boys, are often disorderly and so of course are the demons. But God's great creation is wonderfully orderly. We are lucky here on Lindisfarne that we can see the stars so well, especially on a winter's night. Look up at them often, my sons, and praise God for his beauty, his majesty and his wonderful sense of order."

Before the next lesson Chad had been thinking hard about all this and he began with a question.

"Father, you know you said how the stars could speak to us of God's wonderful order? Do you think we can let other things in creation speak to us of God? What about the more frightening things, like thunder and lightning?"

"Yes, my son," said the teacher, "we certainly can. Remember that both our Christian faith and all parts of creation come to us from the same God. It would be very odd if we could not use what

18

we call 'creation' to help us think about our faith. You mention thunder and lightning, Chad. Well, most people are a little afraid of thunder and lightning. But what we should really fear is the Day of Judgment, of falling away from our Christian faith and life." Then he laughed. "But if anyone wants to make use of a terrific thunderstorm as an occasion to reflect on the Day of Judgment, then I would say that he was making good use of a heaven-sent opportunity."

John, I'm glad that I have been able to remember that conversation in school. Chad was the dearest friend of my life, but I did not see him again after he went away to become Bishop of the Mercians, and it is more than 20 years now since he died. But after he died I heard a story told by his own monks which brought all this back. It seems that Bishop Chad used a thunderstorm exactly as our teacher had suggested. At the first crack of thunder he would lay aside whatever he was doing and begin to pray. As the storm got worse he prayed all the harder.

If it finished and rumbled all around he went into his little chapel, prostrated himself and prayed with all his heart and soul. His monks knew that he wasn't particularly timid about thunder, so they asked why he behaved like this. His answer was, "I use it as a God-given opportunity to reflect on the Day of Judgment which we should fear rather than any danger on earth." An answer coming straight from the schoolroom here on Lindisfarne! You see, John, we were well taught here: we really were. Even for blockheads like me the lessons were interesting. For Chad they were meat and drink; he lived for the time in school.

"If the world is so orderly, Father, why does God upset the order when he does miracles?" This question was from Eata, who was always very orderly in mind.

"God certainly does miracles, my son, and certainly they are surprising to us, but we mustn't suppose from our reaction that they upset God's order. Perhaps, if we knew everything, we should see that they don't. But what we can often see is that miracles take things a little further along the lines of creation. For example, we know that the body contains blood and we know we drink water.

19

We believe that the body takes the water and turns it into blood. So, you see, water can become blood; so if God takes the water of the River Nile and turns it into blood he is simply doing, without the body, what he had made the body able to do. Or, for another example, we know that wine comes from a vine, and the vine takes in water. The vine takes in water and turns it into wine. So, when Christ turned the water into wine at the marriage feast he was only doing without a vine exactly what he gave the vine power to do. And if only we knew more we might be able to say that all miracles can be seen within God's creative will, not opposed to it."

Caelin meanwhile was thinking about something nearer at hand than vines; Caelin was the really practical one among us.

"Father, what are tides?"

"Well, Caelin, there have been many suggestions about why the sea moves the way it does. Some people have thought there is a deep lake under the whole world, from which all the seas and rivers take their water, and that at certain times more water flows out from this lake and causes the tide to rise. But we think this isn't possible, because if it were so then the sea would rise everywhere at the same time, and those of us who live beside the sea know very well that it doesn't! Other people have thought there is a natural ability in water to increase and decrease. Truthfully, I can't tell you. But this much is clear. It has something to do with the moon. We don't know what or why, but we do know that the tide moves with the moon, so to speak, and that it is highest just after a full moon and lowest, even at its high moment, when the half-moon appears. We know this by observation. It is important to see what we can see just by looking. Perhaps later people will know more."

Cynebil, who was a bit of a dreamer, had thoughts above tides. "Father, do people go to heaven or hell when they die? And what is heaven?"

"My dear sons, it is very important to realise that God has made us able to turn away from him and, if we do, that is hell. So something of hell is possible in this life. Certainly people can go to hell when they die if they have finally turned against God. Hell is often

20

pictured as fire, and by God's grace we need never know more of it than the way it has been pictured. And of course people can go to heaven but, Cynebil, I don't know if this happens immediately after they die, or even if that question makes sense. But I'm sure God wants all of us to go to heaven."

"Where is heaven? Well, traditionally it has been thought of as right up there, beyond the clouds and mountain tops, in a purer and better and calmer place than anything we know here. But wherever and whatever it is the important thing is this: that we shall be with God, and with the angels, and with the saints, and with our friends; and we shall be happy and able to return God's love. We must always remember that we human beings lost the right to heaven through sin and that our salvation was won back for us by our Lord Jesus. And salvation is not only for us humans. We think that the world around us was spoilt by our sin, the sun, the moon and the earth, and none of these is now quite what God created it to be. The whole world awaits for redemption. And in what we call heaven, my children, the whole of creation is redeemed."

At this point I remember that I looked up sharply, and our teacher caught my look and my meaning.

"Yes, Egfroth, the whole of creation: this means you and your cat. Don't ask me what Pangur will be like in heaven, because I can't imagine it. But then, Egfroth, I can't quite imagine you in heaven either, but that doesn't mean you aren't going there! No, boys, seriously we must love and value the world God has given us, because God loves it and calls it very good. All that he has made will one day be incorporated into his Kingdom, except for any angels and people who deliberately turn away."

After this lesson I went and found Pangur. I made him sit looking up into the sky and told him that one day he would go to heaven. I think he must have liked the idea because he purred loudly – but then, he always did that when I hugged him.

This was the kind of teaching we were given by our Irish teachers, Brother John. I didn't know I had remembered so much. I must have taken in more than I thought and now it is all coming back.

In many ways I was easily frightened when I was a child, brother. I didn't tell the other boys, of course. But I found our Irish teachers so calm, so reassuring. Sometime, when I lay awake on a winter's night and heard the wind howling and the sea roaring, I used to always feel swept away by nameless fears. Then I would think about what we were taught and especially about the people who taught us, for I have always been more easily impressed by people than by ideas, and I would feel comforted and go to sleep.

As so, brother, for my first few years in the monastery I was happy enough. My family came to see me sometimes. I didn't go home often, though I did go for my second sister's wedding; increasingly 'home' for me was the monastery. Here I had more friends than I ever had before. I began to realise how much bigger the world was than I had ever thought. I began to understand my Christian faith. I tried very hard not to drop things, or break things, or get things wrong, and while we were children the monks were very tolerant. Because my singing was appreciated I worked hard to try to memorise the strange words we sang, and gradually they began to take on meaning. Only sometimes was I the worst dunce in the school. And out of school Pangur and I were inseparable. So I felt I did well enough, and was accepted, and in church, and out of it when they let me, I trilled away like a lark. Yes, I remember being happy.

Until the day it happened. Of course I was aware that my body was changing and I was growing up. Of course I knew in my mind that it was inevitable. Still I wasn't really prepared and it happened to me, not gradually, as it does to some, but suddenly. One day, in church, in the middle of a solo, on a top note, my voice broke.

The monks were kind, of course, and so were the other boys. But I don't think anyone quite knew my devastating sense of loss, of bereavement even. And for me this began one of the most difficult periods of my life, as I'll tell you when we meet again.

After my voice broke, John, I went through a very bad time: a misery to myself and others.

I don't mean that I deliberately set out to hurt anyone, not even myself. I was far too timid to turn into an open rebel. But I felt robbed of the particular place and value I had had, and I couldn't easily believe that there was any other value in me.

So I withdrew myself to nurse my hurt. Church services were very difficult to me. No one told me not to sing, but it was uncomfortable, and I knew there were people who advised boys not to sing until their voices settled. So I attended church feeling defiant and stood there with my mouth shut. I sat in school with my mouth shut too and didn't ask any questions. I know I acted as if I was no longer interested. I was as late for school as I dared to be. I shuffled in my place. Some of the teachers I knew were giving me concerned looks and, with some, concern was turning to anger; though, looking back, I think they were astonishingly patient. I had been quite outgoing to the other boys in the past, telling them stories from my grandfather's fund of stories and joining in everything. I knew that Chad was getting worried; I didn't want to hurt him because I truly loved him but I had to be brusque. "You don't understand, Chad," I said. "You are clever. You are good at everything, but I was good only at one thing. What use am I here?" It was all self-dramatization, Brother John. Actually I had learned to be useful at quite a few of our daily tasks. I had learned to be careful and to do a few things actually quite well. But now I couldn't be bothered to be careful, so again I began to drop things and spill things and to get into trouble. Only Pangur loved me, I thought. And he did: he wasn't bothered by all these human complications.

I withdrew into myself. I spent more time alone. And, like many when real life isn't too good, I filled my mind with dreams. Over and over again I told myself that story about the unpopular boy in the monastery, for whom Saint Columba had predicted a great future. Was there a great future for me? I saw myself as an adventurous monk like Columba, going off to found my own monasteries beyond the seas. I saw myself as a great preacher, drawing the admiring crowds. I saw myself as a great miracle worker. I told all these dreams to Pangur, and he purred.

I don't quite know how long this unhappy phase lasted, John. Several months; probably not much more. Aidan was away for most of this time, on long missionary journeys, and I never felt the monastery was quite the same when he wasn't there. Mostly I conformed to the Rule with a sigh and a grumble. But one night I broke it, and it happened to be a night when Aidan was there.

It was a night late in June – a beautiful night, one of those nights here when it never gets dark, when the last of the sunset seems to merge with the first of the dawn. I lay awake in my bed in our hut, feeling very unhappy. The monastery was quiet; some of us were asleep, and some of us praying. I lay, listening to the silence, wondering when anything would improve. I had sharp ears. I heard in the distance on the other side of the Island the sound of singing. I didn't think it was angels, brother: angels do not come for the likes of me. I knew what it was – seals!

I am sorry for those who have never heard the grey seals sing, brother. Oh yes, I had heard it before, and many, many times since. But neither before or since has it had the magic for me of that particular night. I knew I wasn't supposed to leave the monastery. But rebellion suddenly boiled up in me. Quietly, without waking Chad, but stopping to pick up Pangur who, bless him, was too sleepy to make any noise, I crept out of the hut across the monastery and strode out to the north of the Island.

I sat down on a rock, looking out to sea. The tide was out, the rocks were black in the remains of the sunset; the rocks were covered with seals and they were singing.

Brother I must have sat there for two or three hours, Pangur on my lap. The singing was continuous, but not all the same. Seals sang solos, just as I used to do. Some had high voices, some low; sometimes groups seemed to sing together; sometimes, as far as I could tell, they all sang. I longed to stand up and answer them, but I couldn't. Anyway I felt as if I was spying on a different world, which I couldn't spoil or break into. I longed to know what they were singing about. I knew what we sang about in church, but what about them?

I had no sense of time, but I realised dawn was breaking, that the tide was rising again; I saw the seals slip from the rocks and swim away. But those few hours had soothed some of the wretchedness inside me and I turned to go back to the monastery, Pangur all the while nestling on my arm.

But there was something I had forgotten. Night prayers! Chad had woken up and found I was not there; he had been worried about me for some time since I seemed so miserable, and when I didn't appear for night prayers he had done the sensible and responsible thing and told Aidan. The monks were just about to organize a search party when I turned up. It had truly never occurred to me, self-centred as I was at that time, that anyone would worry about me; indeed I hadn't intended to stay away long enough to be missed, but the music had enthralled me. Aidan looked at me without a smile. 'Go to your bed,' he said. 'You and I must talk tomorrow.'

So the next day we talked, and I shall never forget it. He was not nasty; he never was; but he was very serious, even stern. He told me he had noticed my disruptive behaviour for some time; he knew that I was growing fast and could not help being clumsy. But he asked me straight whether some of it was done on purpose. I had to tell him the truth. Some of it was on purpose, some of it just 'don't care'. But I also found myself for the first time able to talk – about what the loss of my treble voice meant to me, how I felt I had lost also the appreciation I had loved so much, how there was so little else I could be good at. Aidan encouraged me to talk; he seemed to really understand but he remained stern. "My son," he said, "I know it has been hard. But tell me honestly, do you wish to stay here or not?"

It was the first time it occurred to me that I might be asked to leave the monastery, and I turned to ice. No, I did not want to leave, definitely not. Then, he said, I must learn to do my work and play my part properly, whatever my feelings. We are here to do God's

25

work, he said, and we do it as well as we can.

He was quite definite with me. And I came away from that interview feeling clean again, not quite happy but as if I might be happy, and quite determined to have another go at it.

From then on things improved.

The other boys were really good to me, but I think they were also pleased that a corner had been turned.

There was no kind of punishment or public disgrace for me. Only I was made to realise that I had been playing with fire. And I was helped to be different. So, from that day, although never a highly competent person, I have tried to give what I can whatever my feelings.

So the time came, for each of us individually, when we were considered old enough to go out with experienced monks on mission. For Aidan this was a very important moment in our training. He always talked personally to us about the mission and its methods before we went, and every boy, on his first occasion, went out with Aidan himself.

I hadn't realised at the time how unusual he was, Brother John. I was too inexperienced to be able to reflect on the quality of his approach to people. But looking back on it now, from the standpoint of old age, I can see that two things stood out.

First, he was totally serious, definite and committed about his Christian faith. To those who were not Christians he and his monks had something to give or, as I suppose they would have said, God had something to give through them. They had come to our land in order to give and of the preciousness of the gift there was no doubt. I think a lot of their serenity lay in this total confidence in their work.

But secondly, Aidan had an enormous respect for people exactly as they were, whether Christian or not, and he managed to convey this respect to them. He never felt that he, as the giver, could look down on them as receivers. Indeed, I doubt if that was the way it seemed to him. He had never thought that he had come to give people God, only a message from God that they had not so far heard. He knew that God was here before he came and that each person was already God's loved child. He genuinely believed that the other person might have something to give. So he always listened to people, really listened to them. He knew also, and he taught us, that there were different ways of offering a gift, and that some ways of giving actually helped people to receive.

I didn't realise at the time how very complicated was the situation into which he had come. Obviously I knew that there were British and there were English; there were those already Christians and those still pagans. I suppose I knew that Aidan's friendship with King Oswald was both his greatest advantage and his greatest drawback. Of course I realised that some of the British might hate him because he had been invited by the English conqueror. I came to see that others, English or British, might rush to accept the faith because the King favoured it, without any genuine conversion. Altogether I could see that the missionaries needed great discernment and patience as well as courage. I'll tell you, brother, as much as I can remember of the teaching he gave us before we went out. For this was the essence of his work and his heart was wholly in it.

First he said, "Don't expect all people to be alike or to react in the same way. If they are willing to talk always start by finding out what the person already believes. People, including children, are not blanks with empty minds. We must not treat them as if what they have believed so far doesn't matter.

"Suppose the people we meet are British Christians. They could well be nursing deep hurts. For one thing they are conquered and we are on the side of the conqueror they hate. For another thing remember that the British were Christian before the Irish; that British missionaries were among those who took the faith to Ireland: and that the British were Christians long before the English. Think how they are going to feel if an Irishman, or worse still an Englishman, talks to them as if they knew nothing of the faith. To me they might want to say, "My family was Christian when yours was still in the bogs!" or to you "when your ancestors

27

were still savages in the forests of Germany!" And that might well be true! Whether the British Christians we meet know a lot or a little about their faith they are still bound to feel that they got there first. So we won't be surprised if we get opposition or insults from some of them. But never insult them back. Try to understand their anger. If you are getting nowhere say good-bye politely and simply move gently on.

"We might meet British pagans. Try to find out why they are still pagans for they have lived with Christianity in their society for some time. Of course it doesn't follow that they have ever really considered it or even know much about it, but they are likely to have some idea. Perhaps they have felt threatened by it in the past, or they simply prefer the old ways. We are very likely to meet English pagans too. Some of them might really have no knowledge of Christianity, nor even heard the word. To them at first it might be interesting simply as 'news'. That's all right; we try to build on that. Others might already have some curiosity about it especially if they have heard that the King is very keen on this, to them, new religion.

"But with all pagans we try not to make them feel that we think they are quite wrong and that their beliefs and ours are completely opposed. Because they aren't; pagans often have a vivid sense of God, of a life beyond all different forms of living beings, and of a need for humans to find and keep their place. They ask the same questions as we do about the meaning and purpose of life. We don't patronise pagans. But we can tell them that we have something more to offer, a message of love and self-giving of God that goes beyond what they have so far known.

"Some of the people we meet will be ex-Christians: people who have accepted the faith and given it up again. They might be people who became Christian in the days of King Edwin but abandoned their faith when it seemed that the Christian God had deserted him in battle and he was killed. Conversations with them can be very difficult. They could be angry, feeling that they were prepared to trust the Christian God and he had let them down. They might explode in anger at us. We are prepared for that and we try hard not to be angry back. Try to get them to see that God didn't desert King Edwin, because God never promised that those who believe in him would have everything easy or always be successful. See what happened to God's Son, Jesus! But I know that this is one of the hardest things to get across. People are so used to thinking that God is like a good, just king who will reward loyalty with success. It is natural for them to feel angry that God treated Edwin as he did.

"Some of these I have called ex-Christians perhaps really did want to be Christian and are now ashamed that they gave up so soon. Try to get them to see that there is a way back. God understands; God forgives. Tell them the story of Peter's denial of Christ at the time of his trial. If Peter could begin again so can they. They can be Christian again.

"And some perhaps have been secret Christians, keeping their faith in their hearts, but not finding any way to express it or make it grow. These may be truly pleased that there are Christian missionaries here again and may both offer us help and be strengthened by us.

"So this is our method. We never simply walk past anyone in the lanes. Always greet people pleasantly and see if you can get into conversation. If you feel that people are welcoming find out where they live and we'll make a point of going there. But if they rebuff you simply say good-bye pleasantly and get ready to meet the next group. It isn't always easy. In fact it is very difficult if you are feeling tense and rejected. But this is our method. It doesn't threaten people and it leaves them free to choose."

That is what he taught us in those early days and that is how he himself worked. He wouldn't ride a horse. He wanted to be on the same level as the people he met. I heard that one of the kings once gave him a horse, because somehow the king couldn't think it right that a bishop who ranked as a nobleman should walk like a peasant. I heard that Aidan took the horse from the king and I can believe that he did, even though he didn't want it, because he always tried to accept what people offered. It would have been a very fine horse, I'm sure. But Aidan then gave it away to a beggar. When the king was naturally a bit cool about this Aidan said, "Surely that son of a mare is not more to you than that son of God." Those were his exact words, brother, because his chaplain was there and heard them and told us; and even the king agreed that he was right.

It's hard to put into words, but Aidan always had this knack of making the person he was speaking to feel good about himself and about the possibilities that Christianity offered to him. It's quite something to make a beggar feel that he is, or he will be, a son of God.

So we learned to be missionaries. We went out with the older monks and we boys also practised on each other, always seeking the right approach and the right response to whatever the other might say. I also practiced on Pangur but I'm afraid he came into a group that Aidan hadn't mentioned, that of 'pagan-completely-not-interested'!

If we ever got depressed about our failure to make progress with someone or with the mission in general Aidan used to say, "You have often watched dawn on a winter's day on Lindisfarne: how slowly and magically and yet surely the light comes and the colours change. You can understand the growth of faith in a person or people by watching a slow dawn."

I suppose one of the saddest days for me personally, while I was still a boy in the monastic school, was the day my friend Chad left. I don't mean he left the monastic life, of course. Quite a number of boys in the school were competent in their studies, much more competent than I was, but Chad was really bright. He loved learning more than anyone I have ever known. Aidan knew this and one day he spoke to Chad about it.

"My son," he said, "You have learned everything now that this school can teach you and yet you thirst to learn more. If you agree, I shall send you to Ireland."

Ireland! Brother, we knew that the big monasteries in Ireland were far more advanced in study than we could ever be. The Lindisfarne school trained us well to be monks and missionaries and it gave me as much as I could take, and even a little more.

But Chad was different. I could see that the thought of Ireland opened up a vast new wonderful world for him.

So Chad went to Ireland and I didn't see him again for a number of years. When he left I tried to smile and wish him well but that night, alone in the little hut that he and I had shared ever since I first came to the monastery, I couldn't keep back the tears. Pangur in my arms got really wet that night! But I remembered what Aidan had said, that we are here to do God's work whatever our feelings, and the next day I concealed my swollen eyes and went about my work as usual.

As for Chad, he had a marvellous time over there. He told us afterwards how many English and continental students were there, and how generous the Irish monks were to them all. They allowed them to move from monastery to monastery learning all they could from various masters. They gave them all they needed: board and lodging, books and tuition, so freely. Chad had nothing but praise for the Irish Christians; he said they were so committed, so whole-hearted and so adventurous.

I think that Chad's student days in Ireland were among the happiest of his life. I knew that he could live in a different world – the world of the mind – that I could never enter. He knew it too, but never, ever, was he anything but friendly, kind and caring to me. Although, later, we saw each other only occasionally we knew that those early days at Lindisfarne had created a bond that nothing could break. His death came first, as I'll tell you; now that my own death is near I think a lot about Chad.

Thinking about Chad as a student, Brother John, has reminded me of something he told me after his return from Ireland, about another young Englishman who did not return and never will. I don't mean he is dead; indeed, I think he is still alive. His name is Egbert. It seems that he too went over to Ireland and got to know Chad well; for at least part of Chad's time there they were students at the same monastery. However, there was an outbreak of plague and Egbert caught it. In his illness he was aware of his past sins and prayed desperately to be allowed to live longer to make amends, and vowed that if he recovered he would never return home but

31

live as an exile for the rest of his life. He vowed to give a lot of time to prayer and to fast frequently. Chad certainly trusted him and believed that he would keep this vow for his lifetime.

I just said that he vowed to live as an exile, but that wasn't the word Chad used. Chad, and presumably Egbert himself, spoke of living as a 'pilgrim for the Lord'. I mention this word because it was a word Aidan used a lot to explain to us the vocation of a monk and a missionary. In fact it was a word a lot of the Irish used. To them it didn't mean going on a journey to a holy place as people go to Rome or even, now, here to Lindisfarne. These modern pilgrims always expect and hope to go home again. No, pilgrimage for Christ, among the Irish, meant taking God's hand and going out into the unknown. It meant leaving home, family, country – everything that makes us feel safe – and letting God choose our way and our end. To leave family and native country for ever! I have never been called to do that, brother, and I can't help thanking God that I haven't because I don't think that I would have had the courage. I can't even imagine a life away from the place where I was born. So I give all honour to Egbert, and sometimes I wonder where he is now and what he had done with his life.

The first real jolt that we got in the monastery from the outside world was when King Oswald was killed in battle, fighting against Penda, King of the Mercians.

Of course I had always known that kings die in battle. As my grandfather would have said, that was what they were for! Kings and nobles were fighters; boys born into that class were trained for nothing else; it was the natural order of life. In fact it wasn't until our present King Aldfrith came to the throne that I realised that it was possible for a king to have peaceful interests. He's the only one I've ever heard of who just doesn't want to fight.

But King Oswald was a real loss to us. He had been so much part of our life. We all knew the story of how he invited the monks of Iona to Northumbria, of how Aidan had come with his twelve men, had been offered his choice of a monastic site and had chosen Lindisfarne. Aidan himself told us that. But there was a prelude to that which Aidan did not tell us: we learned it from some of the other Irish monks. Apparently when the monks of Iona first received Oswald's message telling them that he was now King of Northumbria and would like them to send a mission they were thrilled. They considered carefully who should be sent as leader. A senior monk called Corman was much respected; he was strong, clear-headed, with a dominant personality. He seemed the obvious choice. So he came over with twelve monks. But it didn't seem to work. He didn't understand us English people; he got across us; I think he must have been a bit of a bully and we didn't like being shouted at. Eventually he saw that it was no use and he returned to Iona. He blamed us Northumbrians for his failure and called us stupid and obstinate. So the monks held a meeting and Aidan spoke up. "Brother," he said, "don't you think you tried to go too fast? If you had been gentler might you not have got further?" That sealed Aidan's fate. I think he must have known he was volunteering for the job. So he was sent over here, and we know how well he succeeded. But Aidan would never have told us that story himself. He never liked drawing attention to other people's failures. And none of us ever asked him about Corman, but we were glad to know the story all the same.

I suppose poor King Oswald must have felt embarrassed when Corman went home, as if he was responsible for his stupid and obstinate people! So no doubt he was delighted when Aidan appeared. He was so friendly to us. We knew that Aidan often went over to see him at Bamburgh, and sometimes the King and a few nobles came to us. Not that we did anything special for them when they came. Aidan wouldn't have thought that right. They prayed in our church and if they wanted to stay for a meal they had to eat whatever we were eating.

So we often saw King Oswald and we admired him a lot. His support was very important. One way he helped must have seemed a bit unusual for a king: he taught the monks the English language! Of course Aidan and his monks spoke Irish and the people round here spoke English. Except the British of course. Their language was rather like Irish, but not exactly the same, I understand. But English was a completely different language. The King of course spoke English but had learnt Irish when he was a boy in exile. I once heard that in the very early days Aidan used to speak to groups of nobles in Irish and the King stood by him and translated into English. That must have been very impressive. But obviously our Irish monks had to learn English before they could go tramping in the lanes.

King Oswald was a real Christian, as I have heard. One story I'm sure was true as everybody was talking about it when it happened. It was Easter Day. Aidan had gone to dine with the King at Bamburgh. Easter dinner was always very special after the long fast of Lent and no doubt the King and his nobles were looking forward to a rather delicious meal. Then, just as Aidan stood up to say grace, a commotion was heard outside the castle and one of the king's servants came in to say that a great crowd of poor, hungry people were there asking for alms. King Oswald gave it all away – food, silver plate and all – to the beggars. We don't know what the king's nobles thought when they saw their dinner disappearing. But Aidan thought it was marvellous. He blessed the hand that had done this generous deed. And you know, John, they say that the hand still survives, at Bamburgh. That may well be. Oswald's skull certainly survives. We have got it here on Lindisfarne, as you know.

Oswald's death happened a long way from here and it took some days for the news to reach us. We knew he had gone to fight, and battles can always go either way. So we were sad rather than surprised when we heard the news. Aidan was very sad, for he had lost a personal friend. Yet, as my grandfather always told me, kings do die in battle. Perhaps even though Oswald was a Christian, it was still the way he preferred to die, and since he died fighting against a pagan many people have called him a Christian martyr. We heard that his last words were a prayer for his soldiers' souls, and that was certainly a Christian way to die.

All sorts of stories circulated after King Oswald's death. It is said that the sick, people and animals, were cured both by earth from the spot where he died and by bits of the wooden cross he had put up on the battlefield, the day before he fought the battle that made him king. If those healings are genuine, brother, then no doubt he is a real saint in heaven and perhaps continues to work in some way there to help us. But here in the monastery, when we first heard the news of his death, our feelings were of sadness mixed with anxiety about what would happen to us next. But King Oswiu took the throne and, although I have never felt quiet as warm about him as I did about Oswald, at least for many years we were protected and our life went on much as before.

CHAPTER 4   DECISIONS

Not all the boys in our school stayed on to become monks in our monastery. Wilfrid didn't, for one, but I'll tell you about Wilfrid later, John. Aidan never thought that it was automatic that we should stay. He never tried to keep any boy against his will, nor any boy who was clearly unsuitable. But he did want English monks, priests, missionaries – even a handful of bishops – and the school was there to provide them.

I was about 18 and had left my silly stage well behind me when Aidan first began to speak to me about my own decision. Always he stressed that I was free to decide, but not free to put off the decision forever.

"The only really important thing in life," he said, "is to do God's will. If God calls you to leave the monastery, perhaps to marry, then do that. If God calls you to stay then we shall ask you to commit yourself." He began to talk to me about the life of a monk as he saw it.

"To be a monk is one way, and only one way, of being a Christian. It is the best way for you if God calls you. Don't expect to hear a voice from heaven – though you might; God can do what he likes. But you have had time to get to know our way of life. Does it seem worthwhile? I know we give up a lot, but then so does everyone who sets out to do great work. And we do set out to do great work: we believe in the task God has given us.

"Think of life as a journey. Some people will only start on a journey if they know where they are going and when they are coming back. But life isn't like that, though we Christians do know where we are going. We are going towards great joy and great fulfilment in God's kingdom. This life is a road, and nobody settles down to live forever on a road. There is no security here. Remember how quickly and unexpectedly life can come to an end. Even those who live longest are really not here for very long. There is no point in looking for a permanent home or lasting happiness here.

"You know a lot of Bible stories. Remember how God called

Abraham from a comfortable life to move down to the Promised Land? That was the beginning of the people of Israel but what would have happened if Abraham had said, "No"? You know how God called the people of Israel out of Egypt to go with him into and through the wilderness? You know how the Lord Jesus called disciples to leave all and follow him? This is the Christian life: adventuring with God, putting your hand into God's hand to go where he leads. We call this 'pilgrimage' and anyone can do it. Some will be led by God to a life of quiet faithfulness at home; others will be led to a life of excitement and adventure wherever God chooses to take them.

"When I came here, my son, I did in one sense know what I was coming to. I knew that King Oswald had invited us, the monks of Iona, to be missionaries here. But I couldn't imagine how we would do it, where we would live, or anything about it. We who came simply gave ourselves to God. We didn't even know if we would arrive safely in Northumbria. We knew only that we had to set out. That is pilgrimage. Many other monks have gone on pilgrimage knowing less that we did: not knowing at all where God would take them or what God willed them to do. But they went. To live like this really is to take God seriously and let him make our choices and guide our way. If you become a monk you are giving yourself to this way of pilgrimage."

Aidan also spoke to me about all that a monk gives up: marriage and family life.

"When you come back from a mission I have seen sometimes, Egfroth, how troubled you are in mind. As you walk the lanes you see many attractive women. You get a mental picture of a home, a wife, children, comfort. Don't blame yourself for feeling this; it is inevitable; you are a young and healthy man. Don't blame the women either; God made them attractive, and that was not to tempt us into sin, even though it happens. I know you are good with children. I have seen how when we meet a family group in the lanes we may talk to the parents but the children come to you. As I said when you first came here, the monastery isn't a prison. If God calls you to marriage you can go with our blessing.

But you must decide. Think like this: no-one can have everything in life. Any choice means giving something up. You see what we have given up; you also see what we are called to achieve. So think, pray, and make your choice."

Since then, brother, though I have still struggled, I have felt freedom. I know that women are beautiful and I can even thank God for their beauty. Sometimes I have felt pain, but have been able to say, "I have made my choice." I know that some monks can solve this kind of problem only by hate. They pretend to hate women for existing and being a distraction. But although Aidan never pretended that things were easier than they are he never solved a problem by hatred. He liked and respected women and their gifts. But for us nothing must get in the way of the work.

We always had lots of visitors at the monastery. Some would stay for a long time. Indeed some came here to die. I remember, when I was about 21, a particular nobleman came here to die, and I remember him, not for himself, though I'm sure he was a nice enough man, but for the young attendant he brought with him. Wilfrid! He was about 14 at the time: very good-looking, very charming, very polished in manner. He had been one of the queen's favourite attendants and she sent him to look after this dying man. I'm sure Wilfrid did that properly. I have no reason to think otherwise. But it was clear that he had ideas for his own future. Everyone could see that he was both gifted and ambitious. When Wilfrid realised there was a school here he asked to join it, and Aidan accepted him. He'd been born into a noble family and had learned the warrior's way. But he wanted something different and although he had not seen writing until he came here he set himself to learn, and did he learn fast! No doubt he was very intelligent and very determined. Of course, since I was no longer a pupil in the school when Wilfrid came, and no one thought of making me a teacher, our paths didn't often cross. I don't want to read back into history some of the problems that have surrounded Wilfrid since. So I will just say, brother, that I admired everything he had: birth, brains, beauty; and I knew that I had nothing he could admire. He was always perfectly civil to me as to everyone. But he made me feel uneasy and complicated.

As you know, brother, I'm a simple man: I like to know what I feel about people and with Wilfrid I didn't.

Another visitor we had to the monastery about this time was a woman. We quite often had women as visitors to the monastery, especially if they needed any help. We know that Aidan had respect for women and a high opinion of their abilities. Our monastery was for men and our school was for boys, he explained, because we were really founded for mission and women could not be expected to tramp the lanes as we did and talk to people they did not know. But Aidan was anxious that women should have the chance to become nuns if they wanted to, and that girls should have some education. So he looked round to find a woman who could perhaps be an abbess. He knew that she would have to be from the aristocracy and either not married or a widow. Most girls were married young and, especially if they were from the noble class, they had little choice whom they married. But because so many men died young, especially from the noble class and on the battlefield, there were always lots of widows. Some women were widows two or three times. It's better under our present king: he's not keen on fighting.

Anyway Aidan found the woman he was looking for, and she visited our monastery. She was tallish, and had what they call 'presence'. I don't know whether she was a widow or not; I haven't heard that. But she was a great success. Apparently there was a monastery some miles down the coast founded by another woman, who then moved away. I don't know anything about her, brother, but Aidan eventually established this lady, Hild, in that monastery. There were both monks and nuns there and she was abbess over both, which is quite usual in our country – or perhaps I should say was quite usual until recently, until Archbishop Theodore and the continentals frowned on the idea. After Aidan died Abbess Hild moved to Deira and founded a large double monastery at Whitby. I've heard that she was very powerful, very learned – and very nice!

But while we are talking about abbesses, brother, I'll tell you about another. You know that King Athelfrith had sons, including Oswald and Oswiu, but he also had daughters, and one of them became an important abbess. Her name was Ebbe and she definitely had been married and widowed. She then wanted to be a nun and obviously, with her high birth, ended up as an abbess. Her monastery was at Coldingham, a few miles north of our big river here. I'll tell you two stories about this monastery. You will be interested in the first one because it concerns your favourite saint, Cuthbert. I wasn't there but I heard about it after Cuthbert died from the monk who experienced it. This is what he said:

"I was a monk at the monastery at Coldingham when Cuthbert came to visit our Abbess Ebbe. Of course at that time no-one knew that Cuthbert would turn out quite so famous, but he was already well-known and we were pleased to set eyes on him. He stayed for several days and, after a day or two, it was noticed that he always slipped out of the monastery after night prayers though he was always there again by morning prayers. Several of us whispered together about where he would go to, and I decided to find out. I don't feel very proud of it now because I was really nothing but a plain spy. Anyway, one night I did follow him, taking care not to be seen. He went down on to the beach and I hid behind a rock. He simply was there all night, in and out of the sea, sometimes standing still, sometimes lifting his arms in prayer, and sometimes gently singing psalms. I was getting very stiff and cold and sleepy behind my rock and nothing interesting was happening, but somehow I couldn't go away. Then, just at first light, he turned and came out of the sea and as he did so two sea otters came up with him and began to play round him. I saw the silhouettes of all three of them, black against the dawning light. I knew it was Cuthbert and two wild otters. Then, suddenly, it wasn't. All that I had ever been taught swept over me: of how God created all life to be in harmony, and then man sinned and the harmony was broken, but in God's plan and God's good time the harmony would be restored by Christ. Suddenly it was Christ himself there in his servant on the beach and not just two otters but all living things. It was for a moment as if I had lifted the corner of a curtain and spied on the Kingdom of Heaven! And so I was flat on my face and shaking violently all over when Cuthbert actually walked up to me. Of course he knew immediately what had happened. But he was gentle with me. "You haven't done anything unforgivable," he said.

40

"But promise me one thing. Don't talk about all this until I am dead." And indeed I haven't. But he is dead now," said this brother, "and I want to talk about it. No other experience has made me feel God so close." Those were his exact words, John.

The other story I have to tell you about Coldingham is not so wonderful and not all happy, but I have to tell it to you because it is part of our history. The Abbess Ebbe was very well respected by those who knew her and I think she was a really good woman. Being part of the royal family she was able to influence even some of the kings for good. I've heard that she was even able to persuade her nephew, King Edgfrith, to release Wilfrid from prison. I know that Wilfrid was very controversial but it wasn't right for him to be shut up in prison. Anyway, she was a good woman. But was she a successful abbess? No doubt in many ways she was. But it seems that towards the end of her life Coldingham did get a bit lax. I don't mean any serious evil, but not living the life as it should be.

The story we heard, John, was that one of the monks of Coldingham was actually warned in a vision about this lax state of affairs. One night he was awake and praying when a heavenly visitant stood by him and said, "I'm very glad to find you at prayer. I can tell you that very few others in the monastery are. Oh yes, they're awake, but far from praying they are chatting to each other about worldly, trivial things. God can't let this mockery of the monastic life go on. One day there will be a reckoning." Then the vision vanished, leaving the poor monk in a terrible state of mind. He couldn't think at all what he ought to do, whether he should keep it to himself and hope it would go away, or whether he should tell someone, or what. Eventually he did confide in another monk who thought the whole thing should be told to the Abbess. Ebbe listened and then made an attempt to pull the place together, which succeeded for a while. But then she died, about 16 years ago, and three years later the monastery was burned down. Of course everyone who was in the know said it was judgment on them. Does God work like that? I just don't know, Brother John, I just don't know.

Occasionally, though not very often, queens have also come to visit here on Lindisfarne. I don't remember any queen before Eanflaed,

Oswiu's wife. Some rather fascinating things are told about her. It is said that she was the very first English person to be baptised in Northumbria. How did this happen? Well, King Edwin, whom I've already mentioned, was of course a pagan when he came to the throne but he wanted to marry the Princess Ethelburga of Kent. She was a Christian, and the marriage agreement included provisions that she would bring a chaplain with her who would be allowed to evangelise and that King Edwin would consider becoming a Christian. She brought Paulinus, who did indeed work as a missionary, and King Edwin kept his word to think about becoming a Christian but he took a long time over it. However one day two important things happened: the queen gave birth to their first child and the king survived a murderous attack on his life. At that point he still wasn't quite ready to be a Christian himself but as a thanksgiving he allowed his baby daughter to be baptised, and she was Eanflaed. Later, of course, the king was baptised with many of his nobles and family, including the lady Hild, who was just a young girl at the time. But when King Edwin was killed in battle Paulinus took the queen and her small children back to Kent, and that included Eanflaed. So she was brought up under the influence of the Roman Christians in Kent rather than the Irish ones here. Later she returned to marry Oswiu and was a good and devout queen. But when she and Oswiu had a daughter that baby was handed in to Saint Hild's monastery to be brought up there, as a thanksgiving for a victory in battle, and when Oswiu died Eanflaed also became a nun at the same monastery.

As far as I know she is still there.

King Edgfrith married twice and we saw both his queens here occasionally. The first marriage was a strange one, so rumour said. This queen Aethelthryth, had previously been married to a nobleman in East Anglia, but she hadn't really wanted either marriage. What she wanted was to be a nun; she had wanted this since she was a girl and would have nothing to do with either husband. So there were no children of either marriage. King Edgfrith got tired of this and allowed the marriage to be dissolved and the Queen to go. In fact she went to Coldingham for a while and then returned south to found her own monastery. The next Queen, Iurminburg, was entirely different! There was nothing 'nun-ish' about her, at least at first. She was really rather worldly and certainly tried to get her own way. Yet even she became a nun in the end, after her husband's death. But I'm in danger of getting things out of order so I'll keep that story till later, brother.

I want to emphasise that our monastery really was open to people, all people, men and women, especially those in trouble. This has never been a remote, secluded island, not even before the fame of Saint Cuthbert brought so many visitors. We never put on anything special for noble visitors. If they came here they wanted to see us as we were and to share part of our life as it really was. Aidan would have thought it quite wrong to treat a beggar differently from a king. He treated both with great courtesy. Hospitality to all was one of the most important lessons we were taught. Every guest must be treated as if he were Christ himself.

I never knew how old Aidan was, John. When I was a child he seemed to me to be both old and ageless. He never changed. But looking back on it now I suppose he must have been about 40 or a little more when he came here, and he was bishop here for about 16 years.

The day he died is branded on my memory. I was about 24 years old at the time. Now that I am old I can dare to say that I loved him; he meant more to me than any other person I have met. Of course I knew he would die, but I didn't expect him to. It made it worse that it didn't happen here. He was away a lot on missionary journeys; he left the day-to-day running of the monastery to others.

It was towards the end of August and quite hot. A messenger came rushing from Bamburgh. Aidan had been taken ill; he hadn't died but he couldn't be moved. He had been leaning against the wall of the church in Bamburgh when whatever-it-was-happened and he just crumpled up and fell. The brothers who were there did all they could; they built a kind of tent over him to shelter him from the weather. He never really recovered consciousness, and on the last day of August, in the early part of the night, he died. The body was brought over here by boat. We all went down to the harbour to meet it and we were all there when he was buried.

Even now, John, I can't say much about those days. I went about stunned. It seemed that he had left us in full health and returned as a body. No chance to say good-bye. No chance to bless us and his monastery as I had been told Columba did at Iona on his last day.

Why did he have to die just then? Apparently towards the end he did say one or two words and among them, once or twice, the name 'Corman'. I've told you the story of Corman, who came from Iona before Aidan and failed to convert us unconvertible Northumbrians. But what was on Aidan's mind that he should say the name 'Corman' so near to his own death?

Afterwards we heard something that might be the clue. You remember that after the death of King Oswald Northumbria again fell into two parts. Oswald's brother Oswiu took the north, Bernicia, and his cousin Oswine took Deira, the south. But people said that Oswiu, from the beginning, wanted to be king of the whole. King Oswine was a particular friend of Aidan; he was the king who gave Aidan a horse, and we know that Aidan thought very highly of him. But King Oswiu was also Aidan's friend. Well, we heard that, shortly before Aidan collapsed, Oswine had been murdered. It's not an uncommon fate for kings and nobles but... the finger of suspicion pointed at Oswiu. Not of course that he stuck in the dagger with his own hand; simply that he organized and encouraged the killing because he wanted the southern kingdom. But to Aidan that would have been the same as murder. People said this was the news that caused Aidan's illness. Both kings were Christians and both were his friends. People said that perhaps among his last thoughts was the thought, "Corman was right. I have taught them nothing. I might as well have stayed at home on Iona."

Of course, if that was what Aidan thought at the end we know he was mistaken. Looking back on it all almost fifty years later we know what he achieved. He was the real founder here, and his work endures.

It's a strange thing, brother, but you know that Aidan's little wooden church at Bamburgh was burned down a few years ago. That in itself isn't strange: wooden buildings lit by candles often burn down. But, so people said, the particular beam against which Aidan was leaning when he was taken ill just didn't burn. So when they built the church up again they built that beam into the wall and there it is. It's as if there's a message in the beam. Aidan died but his work can't be destroyed.

I couldn't bear the thought that he had died in misery of mind, with a sense of failure, and yet I lived with that thought for years. But in the end help came to me unexpectedly from, of all people, Cuthbert. I know, Brother John, that you have a great devotion to Cuthbert because of the way you were healed. But when he first came to our monastery (and of course he came to be in charge; I'll tell you about that later) I was afraid of him. He seemed to

45

be altogether too efficient, too energetic, not quite human. And of course he came at a bad time. A lot of the brothers couldn't stand him at first. Yet I always felt he wanted to be friends with us. One day he went out of his way to talk to me. "Will you tell me," he said, "about how you first came to join the monastery?" So I told him what I've told you about Aidan inviting me to the school. "That's good," he said, "because it was Aidan also who made me decide to be a monk." "Did you know Aidan?" I asked, surprised. "No," he said, "I never spoke to him, though of course I knew all about him; the year he came here was the year I was born. As a youth I thought a lot about becoming a monk. But I didn't do anything about it until I was 16, or it might have been 17. I had agreed to look after a friend's sheep, and there I was on the hillside, lying awake in the warm night and looking up into the sky. I seemed to be all alone in the waking world when I was suddenly aware of a light moving in the sky. Not a shooting star; I've seen those before. No, this light moved downwards to earth and up again, and as I looked I became convinced that this was a group of angels, escorting a human soul to heaven. Brother Egfroth, you can be sure that the next day I eagerly asked the obvious question: who had died? It was the night that Aidan died. I waited no longer. I went straight to the nearest monastery, which was Melrose. It was of course founded by Aidan and I've heard since that you, Egfroth, had a hand in building it. The abbot of course was and is Eata, who I know is an old friend of yours; and the prior at the time was Boisil who until his death was a great friend of mine. But the deciding influence for me was Aidan on his journey from earth to heaven. I like to think that, as I saw him as he went to heaven, so on his last journey he also saw me as I lay on the hillside and, without any voice, he called to me. And so, Brother Egfroth, although you had the great advantage of knowing Aidan personally, we have this in common, that we both became monks because of him."

That is what Cuthbert said to me, Brother John, and it helped me to feel differently about Cuthbert, because he had shared something so precious and so personal with me. It also helped me to feel better about Aidan's death because, even if his last moments on earth had been sad, I could now be reassured that he had gone to heaven and was happy there in the Kingdom of God. And so indeed he must

46

be, for I have never known anyone who gave more single-mindedly to God's Kingdom.

At about the time Aidan died I was thinking a lot about death, brother. A few months earlier my own father had died. That was the first time someone close to me had died, apart from my grandfather, for whom I had felt a child's grief. We had been lucky as a family: although my elder sister's first baby died at birth I never felt I knew him. Babies do die, lots of them, and mothers in childbirth too. But, thank God, my sister survived and had healthy children afterwards. But as I have told you my family were farmers and fishermen, and my father died in an accident at sea. Of course it happens all the time, but it's always a shock: a healthy man goes out to fish and no-one returns, or perhaps a body does return, washed up by the tide. My father's body did return, and I think it's better that way: it's easier to accept the fact of death if you can have a burial.

When it happened someone came and told Aidan, and Aidan told me. He was, as he always was, gentle and sympathetic. He gave me leave to go home immediately and so I did, though there was little I could do: my brothers and sisters and their children were already there. So were several neighbours: people always come together in a crisis. My mother was glad to see me, though she didn't need me. But I brought an important message: since my father had been a Christian, baptised by Aidan himself, the monastery would be responsible for the funeral. She was glad of that, and I was glad that we could commend him to God in a Christian way.

My mother and family were under quite a lot of pressure from friends and distant relatives to bury some grave goods with my father's body. That was always the pagan custom, and many so-called Christians reverted to the custom when there was a family burial. I suppose they might have been trying to have it both ways, or possibly it was just the strength of custom, or maybe the presence of pagan family members that persuaded them. Funeral traditions don't die as easily as people. So some of our friends were a bit horrified that we didn't bury anything in the tomb with my father. After all we were not poor; we could easily have afforded something. But I'm glad my mother stood firm. "He would not have wanted it," she said. "He was a serious Christian." That helped me a lot, brother. I'd never really known what my father thought about religion, though obviously our family would not have been converted if he had not taken the lead. But I had left home at 10, and as I said earlier my father was not a man of many words. It was good to know from my mother that his faith was real.

After that I used to go and see my mother once a year (as did Cuthbert, though in his case it was his foster-mother, he was better-born than I was and had been fostered out as a child). My mother lived to be sixty: a good age. My brothers and sisters are all dead now, but they all lived a reasonable length of time. As a family we were lucky, and I count myself as the luckiest – perhaps I should say most blessed – of the lot.

But to go back to the time of Aidan's death and before I knew of Cuthbert's vision. I couldn't stop myself brooding over the fact that Aidan had died so differently from Columba. You don't know the story of Columba's last day on Iona? Our Irish teachers made sure we knew it well. There are many ways to die, but I think Columba's must have been one of the happiest. For although he lived to old age, older than I am now, he kept his powers of mind and body to the end, though he began to feel tired. Well might he have felt tired after the energetic life he had lived! Mysteriously he knew in advance the time of his end and, as the end approached, he was able to walk round his island and bless all parts of his monastery.

I am not soft on animals, John (except Pangur, of course). But I like the bit of this story about the horse. This beast also was old and, like Columba, had grown old in the service of the monastery. On Columba's last day, as he was resting as he went round blessing the place, the horse came ambling up to him, nuzzled against him, and showed all the signs of grief that a horse can show.

Columba stroked and patted the horse to comfort him. Then he said to his attendant monk, "See, this animal has been granted a knowledge that none of the monks have. He knows that we shall not meet again, and that I shall die today."

Well, John, I think that could be true. Animals do sometimes have a strange knowledge that goes beyond human understanding.

Then Columba spent part of the day writing. He was always so keen on education and his hand must have been much steadier than mine is now. But then it grew dark and he rested a little. But when the bell rang for night-prayers he was up and out of his hut like a flash, running – yes, running at his age – towards the church. He got there first; as the other monks ran they saw a great light in the church, and there they found Columba collapsed before the altar, and so he died.

Don't you think that's marvellous, John? To run to meet your death as to a joyful appointment not to be missed or delayed!

I've heard of a great light shining at the death of others specially close to God. Do you remember that I told you before of the lady Hild, whom Aidan persuaded to stay and be a nun in Northumbria? She was abbess for many years down at Whitby, and a very good and successful abbess she was. I've also heard what a good woman she was: how wise; many famous people used to go and ask her advice. Well, she died after a long illness; it must be almost 20 years ago. I've heard that when she died a nun in a daughter-house some miles away awoke to see, apparently, the roof open and a great light pouring in, it wasn't until the next day that they knew that Hild was dead.

I'm sure that since the beginning of the human race people have been saying: there is only one way into this world and many ways out of it. I think of the people I have known who have died: my father in drowning, Aidan in distress, Oswald in pain, Cedd suddenly of the plague, Hild after 6 years' illness… Who can say what is the good death we all hope for? But I like the Columba story and I just wish that Aidan had died more like that.

I've never been given visions, brother, of great lights or anything else, and I suppose most ordinary Christians haven't either. But sometimes you hear of someone who seems quite ordinary who has had a very strange experience, even an experience of life after death. There is a monk at Melrose, who must be my age or somewhat younger, called Drycthelm. As far as I know he is still alive but now lives as a hermit in a secluded corner of that monastery. For some years he has been very ascetic. But he didn't join the monastery when he was young. For much of his life he lived as a good, ordinary layman, married and had children. But one day he fell ill and apparently died. The family were sitting round the bed, no doubt consoling each other and planning the funeral when, suddenly, the dead man sat up. All the relatives fled shrieking, except, I heard, his wife, who loved him dearly and would stay with him alive, dead, or resurrected! To her he told the story of what he had seen beyond death. He would never talk much about this to others, unless he was convinced that they were looking for God seriously and not just looking for excitement. He explained to his wife that, as a result of his vision, he must now live differently. He made proper provision for her and for his family, then he asked to join the monks of Melrose. Of course he told them why he was joining and since we know them well we heard about it too. Once Drycthelm became a monk he also became extremely devout, as a result of his vision. This is what he said about it:

"I knew that I was lying very ill in bed and then, suddenly, I wasn't. I found myself in an open space, walking towards the sunrise. There was a man or an angel walking beside me. I didn't discover who he was but he acted as my guide. As we walked we seemed to be crossing a deep valley. On one side I could see flames of fire shooting up and feel the heat. On the other side was hail, storm and snow and coldness beyond anything I had ever felt. I then saw that there were people in the heat of the fire and people in the cold of the snow. They seemed to be leaping from one side to the other, as the heat or the cold got too much to bear. I thought, 'Surely this is hell?' but my guide answered my thought, 'No, these people indeed committed some evil deeds, but they repented. They are in pain now, but they will be freed before or at the Day of Judgment.' He led me on and we came to what must be hell indeed where I can hardly describe what I saw of torment, noise and darkness. There he seemed to leave me and I wondered, terrified, if I was abandoned in that place for ever. Then he came back and led me out again into the light. I saw in front of us a great wall and, just as I was wondering how we could climb it, we found ourselves on top.

What a beautiful sight beyond the wall! Fields, flowers and groups of happy people everywhere. But just as I was thinking, 'This must be heaven' my guide again answered, 'No. These are indeed happy people on their way to heaven, but there is more beyond.' Then I saw in front of me a light which made all other lights dim, and smelt a fragrance beyond all fragrance, and heard music beyond all music. I longed to enter that place but my guide turned me round and led me away. 'You must go back now', he said. 'Live to the glory of God and one day you will indeed come here again and stay forever.' The next thing I knew was that I was in my own bed."

That is what Brother Drycthelm said, John. Now the Abbot of Melrose allows him to live a little apart and he lives a very austere life indeed. Perhaps because we live in a cold place the coldness of his vision seems to have impressed him more that the heat. So one of the things he would do, as an ascetic practice, was to go out in winter and stand for a time in the river which borders that monastery. Sometimes there were even little icebergs floating in the river. Of course the local people turned out to look. But if one of them said what they were all thinking, "We don't know how you can stand such bitter cold," he would simply reply, mindful of his vision, "I have known it colder."

Drycthelm wants nothing now except to prepare for the life of heaven. It takes a very powerful experience to cause a person to change his life so much. I respect Drycthelm but I think such visions are given to very few. Most of us prepare for heaven – or don't – by responding, or not responding in our more ordinary lives to the ordinary Christian teaching we are given. And now, at the end of my own life, I feel I can trust myself to God without expecting any actual foretaste of what is coming. Indeed, I have had a foretaste of heaven in the kindness and generosity that has been shown me here.

This talk has been all about death, John. So one more death and then we are done for today. It was a year or so after Aidan's death that my first cat died. It was hard to see him getting older and stiffer and in the end he just lay down and died.

I grieved indeed for Pangur with whom I had shared so much of my early hopes, fears, trials, joys.

Of course the monastery immediately had another cat, also called Pangur. We continued to call all our cats Pangur and in my long life here I have had 7 Pangurs: this is the 7th. I have loved them all, but the first was special because, as Aidan said, he and I grew up together. It was good, as a young person, to have something to hug, someone to confide in. It is good for this old person, too. And I think all the Pangurs have loved me, but perhaps specially the first, and this one, now sitting on my lap purring away.

But when the first Pangur died my mind went back to that lesson in school when our teacher said that all that God had made and loved would somehow share in the Kingdom, including me and my cat. So I have a hope that somehow I shall see Pangur 1 again – and indeed all the others. Two of them died young: one of a mysterious illness while he was still a kitten and the other at about 2 years old just disappeared. The others all lived reasonable cat lives. I know I have loved my cats; I am content to believe that my love for them is a pale shadow compared with the love of the God who made them; and I am content to leave it all to God.

Given that no-one could follow Aidan… we were all left wondering who was to follow Aidan. Of course at that stage we were still Iona's baby, and Iona chose the next bishop who was called Finan. He had been a monk there, and was bishop here for about ten years. I got on all right with him, brother, and I think he was a good and competent bishop. But he wasn't as calm and gentle as Aidan. Some even called him hot-tempered and I do remember a furious row between him and another Irishman called Ronan. This man came here supposedly as our guest but we soon found out that his real intention in coming was to tell us how wrong we were in the way we calculated the date of Easter. This was the first time I was aware there was any problem about Easter. To me it was just Easter; it just happened like so many other things in life. I told you before that our masters in the school here tried sometimes to explain to us about it. But I never let it be a problem to me; I just dozed off until the explanation was over! Now I realised for the first time that it was possible for different Christians to keep Easter on different days, which I could see would cause a lot of bother. Anyway, more about Easter later.

Life on the island was changing. For one thing we were becoming a much bigger community. When Aidan first came he had with him just twelve monks from Iona. This was the Irish way of sending a mission, and it was based on the Gospels of course: a leader and twelve followers. But as soon as Iona realised that these monks were settled, and that Aidan's monastery was likely to succeed, they sent more Irish monks. At the same time Aidan was looking out for English recruits. As well as boys in the school, to be trained up from the beginning, he of course accepted older men if any suitable ones came, and some did. I don't know how many we were by this time, but a good number.

So Finan decided we needed a second church. It was to be quite close to the first church but bigger and more substantial. All the same it was still built in wood with a thatched roof. All our buildings were in wood in those days, brother. It was the Irish way. To us English as well it seemed natural, for we too were happier building in wood and living in wooden houses. We wouldn't have known what to do with stone. When I saw the stone building in Carlisle when I went there with Cuthbert much later and I realised that they were just a remnant from the earlier days of the Romans, I was astonished. Cuthbert later said that York was like that, too. He went there when he was made bishop.

But at the time of Finan our monastery was wood and thatch and nothing else.

Years later, long after Finan's death, this church was dedicated to Saint Peter, and Archbishop Theodore himself came to consecrate it. That was a great day. I think I, and some of the other monks, were a little surprised when we saw the Archbishop. Of course we knew he wasn't English, but he did somehow look so foreign. And he was rather old – at least I thought so then. And of course he was riding a horse. My mind went back to Aidan as it so often did. But to tell you the truth, brother, my mind wasn't really on this occasion. My mind was on Pangur, who that day had gone missing. We never found him. Whether he was scared by the crowds, or even kidnapped by someone in the crowd, who can say? Of course we quickly got another cat, but I had to worry and grieve then. I have grieved for each of them in his turn…

To get back to Finan. I don't remember that he built anything else specially. Of course we were building all the time, because as our number grew we needed more huts, more workshops, more cattle sheds and so on. I was usually on call for this, because by this time I was quite experienced in building such things, as well as being, as I told you, big and strong.

But Bishop Finan did give me some remarkable experiences. When he went outside the monastery as bishop he invited me to go with him more than once. Of course I realised that this was partly because of my size. I could carry luggage and I could frighten off any possible attackers. I never deluded myself that I was invited because of my eloquence or brainpower. But it was good to go. In fact I had not left the monastery since I entered it as a small boy, except to go on mission or occasionally to visit my family, as I have said.

The most exciting time was when we went to baptise Peada and some of his friends. He was the son of King Penda of Mercia and his father had made him sub-king of that part of Mercia lived in by the Middle Angles. Peada was already friendly with Oswiu's son Ahlfrith, who had married his sister. Now he wanted to marry Ahlfrith's sister, Oswiu's daughter, who was called Ahlflaed. King Oswiu was quite happy to allow this, but only on one condition: that Peada and his men became Christians. So Peada came up north to learn all about it. Peada is said to have been so thrilled when he heard all about the promises of the Gospel, such as eternal life in the Kingdom of Heaven, that he declared that he would have the faith even if he could not have the princess. But as things turned out he had both. Our Bishop Finan, with me and others in attendance, travelled to the King's house at Ad Murum, near the Roman Wall and there Peada and his followers were instructed and baptised.

I don't want to sound cynical in my old age, John, but I have often wondered what the Christian faith meant to him and his family, in reality. His father, that old warrior and enemy of ours, Penda, remained an obstinate pagan to the end of his life. But we were told that Penda never objected to anyone becoming Christian, provided they were genuine about it, but he had only contempt for the insincere. But I can't tell you what goes on in men's hearts, and we are told in the Gospels not to judge. All I can tell you is that Peada was baptised, with the noblemen with him, and the marriage went ahead. King Oswiu was there looking really pleased. As for me, it was exciting to be there, even though I went only to carry the baggage. I saw things I had never seen in my life before, particularly the Roman Wall. I'd heard about it, and there it was in front of me, a huge stone wall going right across the countryside. They say it goes from the sea on one side of the country right over to the sea on the other. Why ever did they build it? Some people say that the Romans built it to keep the Picts out. But I don't know if that can be true. I never heard of any Picts as far south as that. So I don't know.

But I do know that when Peada turned to go home again he took with him four Christian priests to help convert his people and one of them was our Cedd. I didn't know the others very well and have forgotten their names. I think only one of them was Irish. They worked hard and successfully among the Angles down there. The Irish priest among them eventually became bishop of the Middle Angles and of the midlands generally, and our Bishop Finan consecrated him. But Cedd didn't stay in Middle Anglia for ever. You see, King Oswiu liked using his influence over other kings to get them to become Christians. Oswiu was a difficult man to understand; I never really felt he could be trusted, but he certainly liked spreading the faith. One of Oswiu's friends was Sigebehrt, King of the East Saxons, who often used to visit Oswiu in Northumbria. Apparently our king used to talk to his visitor long and hard about the superiority of Christianity over paganism. In the end Sigebehrt and his followers gave in, so that was another mass baptism for Bishop Finan to do; again it was at Ad Murum, and again I was taken along and could have a second look at the Roman Wall. Again there were consequences for our Cedd because King Sigebehrt wanted to take a missionary back with him to his kingdom. Oswiu thought no-one would be better than Cedd, so he was persuaded to leave the Middle Angles and go down, with another priest, to begin to convert the East Saxons.

So you see, John, how important Bishop Finan's time was for the spread of Christianity. It was the time when those who had been trained by Aidan reached the age to lead missions to other kingdoms. I was never that sort of person! But I am proud to have had Cedd and Chad among my friends. Aidan would have been pleased – or rather, I should say, is pleased as he watches us and prays for us in heaven.

Seeing so many important pagans become Christian and be baptised made me think about paganism in a way I had never thought before. Now here is a difference between us, John. You were born into a Christian family; you have been a Christian since the cradle; your parents were keen on their faith and that is why you came here to be healed. All your friends were Christian and the word 'pagan' suggests to you something long ago and far away. I think when you have been here a little longer and begin to do missionary work you will find there are still plenty of pagans around.

However I expect they will always seem a little strange to you.

But I was born a pagan, in a largely pagan society. I was a pagan until I was 9 years old. It didn't worry me much at the time! Then I was baptised with the rest of my family, but that wasn't my choice. And because I left home at the age of 10 I never had a proper chance to ask my parents why they decided to become Christians.

You remember that I told you about my grandfather, the one who told me all the stories of the kings. He was a pagan and remained one. He died when I was just 9 years old, shortly before we were baptised. So I don't know what he would have felt about us becoming Christians. Before that we all used to go together to the festivals and they were exciting, but I have now only the haziest memory of that.

Yet I would maintain that my grandfather was a genuinely religious man. I always feel uneasy when people speak as if only Christians could be genuinely religious. I can see you raising your eyebrows slightly at me, and you are wondering what I mean by calling him genuinely religious. I've wondered myself what I mean by it and it's hard to find the right words, but I'll try to explain something of what I felt about him.

I suppose the basic thing was that he believed there is much more to life than we see on the surface. He had a sense of the importance of life itself and its unity. He used and killed animals, of course, as we all did, yet he respected them. I've seen him care for an injured animal or bird as if it was a baby. He seemed to think there is a connection between the life that flowed through him and the life that flowed through them. He went to the festivals and to the pagan holy places and took part as people did. He thought the cult was important and that our work as farmers on sea and land were influenced by it. Life in him was deep and mysterious. He believed in great unseen powers, both for good and evil, and he thought it right to try to live in harmony with the good.

That's about all I can say, John, though I wish I had known him when I was older and could have talked about these things. But it made sense to me when Aidan said we were to respect the pagans we met on our journeys, because in many ways they had the right instincts and asked the right questions. As long as I remember my grandfather I know I shall have a respect for pagans.

But I only wish he could have met Aidan. He did in fact go to listen to Paulinus, the missionary who came up from the south with Queen Ethelberga. She was married to King Edwin and a good deal of the time they lived in the area of York. But Edwin did come up to Ad Gefrin sometimes and Paulinus came with him and preached to large crowds. Large crowds were converted and baptised. But not my grandfather. He described Paulinus to me: an impressive man, dark-haired, with a hooked nose and a slight stoop, who was a convincing and dominating speaker. But my grandfather was not one to change quickly, or to change simply because the King was there, even though, as I have said, he quite admired King Edwin.

Not that Edwin himself changed quickly, according to the stories going about at the time. He had promised the Queen's father that he would think about becoming a Christian, and he did think about it – for some years. Of course a king would not take such a decision without consulting his nobles. My grandfather heard a story, which he told to me, about such a meeting in the King's hall. One of his nobles compared our life here to the flight of a bird, in at one end of the well-lit hall, through the hall and out at the other end. 'In from the darkness; out again into the darkness,' this man had said, 'so if this new religion can tell us more about the darkness let's accept it.' Well, yes, but only if what the new religion says about the darkness is true.

But apparently the chief of the King's pagan priests was converted. He deliberately defied pagan religion by taking a spear in his hand and riding out on a stallion to destroy the temple in which he had previously officiated.

My grandfather didn't like that and I sensed that he didn't really like Paulinus. Perhaps the wound in his leg taught him to go slowly in all things. He lived long enough to see that some of these very new Christians, whom Paulinus had baptised, were disillusioned about the power of their new God when King Edwin was killed in battle, and were turning away from their new faith. My grandfather didn't like that either. 'They ought to have stuck to it,' he said. 'They ought to have given it a real chance. The death of a king in battle is no argument against a religion. Kings always get killed in battle.' Anyway, he never changed. I can now see that he might have got on well with King Penda! I don't know what he made of the story of Jesus… I do wish he could have met Aidan.

Bishop Finan died about ten years after he came to us, and Iona sent a third Irish bishop, Colman. I liked Colman and hoped he would be with us for a long time. But that was not to be. He was our bishop for only three years.

What happened then, Brother John, was so big and important to us here that I think we must keep it for our next talk together.

Chapter 7 Conflict

Iona was always a magical name to us, brother, even to those of us, like me, who had never been there. All our first leaders, including our first three bishops, Aidan, Finan and Colman, were monks of Iona. The other monks who came from there with the three bishops were always telling us stories about Iona and that giant among men, Columba. If any problems arose it seemed natural to us to ask, "What does Iona do? What does Iona think?" We never expected that the supply of Irish bishops and monks would dry up. We were part of an empire, and the centre of that empire was Iona.

Yet, especially for those of us who were not Irish, those of us who were British or English, there must have been a buried consciousness of something else. We knew that Britain had once been part of a different empire, a huge one, ruled from the great city of Rome. We knew that Ireland had not been part of this empire. If we climbed up on the Heugh here on Lindisfarne and looked across to the mainland we were looking towards Iona, where our links were then. But if we turned round and looked across the open sea, somewhere, beyond the horizon, many months' journey away, was Rome, where our links used to be before.

I also knew, and so did the other monks here who were English, that our English ancestors had come from a land nearer than Rome, but still on the other side of that sea. Sometimes I used to stand and just gaze out eastwards and think, 'what is that land like now? Have I perhaps got some distant cousins still living there?' But I didn't expect the wind or the tide to bring me any answer to that!

I don't mean that our Irish monks didn't know about Rome. Of course they did. Before Christianity came to Ireland the Irish were raiding and trading with the fringe countries of the Roman Empire. When Christianity came to them obviously it came from inside the Roman Empire: there was nowhere else it could have come from. But I think that the British, and also the English who had settled in Britain, always had more of a feeling for Rome than the Irish did. Rome had been part of the history of our land; it had not in the same way been part of the history of theirs.

Well, we also always knew of course that we were not the only Christians in the world. But in those days we didn't often meet Christians who were not from the orbit of Iona. So it was a shock when we realised that some other Christians not only did things differently, but even looked down their noses a bit at the way we did things. Still, to most of us it didn't seem a vital question. We were all Christians: surely we could live and let live.

But, brother, as things turned out, we couldn't. Some differences had to be resolved; some decisions to be made. And the way they were made changed the life of our monastery forever.

Part of the problem was the date of Easter. "What?" you say. "Did Christians really quarrel about dates?" Yes, they did, but because this matter was settled long before you were born, brother, you find it hard to imagine. But the date of Easter is important because Easter is our main festival and because so much of our year follows on from the date of Easter. If we Christians couldn't even agree on that, what kind of example would this be to the pagans? So, although explanations of the matter sent me as a schoolboy to sleep as I've told you, I did make another effort to understand when it became really important to us, and I'll try to explain it to you.

Now, Pangur, be still. You know I need my ten fingers for this explanation. You should know that: I've practiced on you enough times. So John, here are my Ten-Easy-Stages-for-Understanding-the-Date-of-Easter-Question.

FIRST: our Lord was crucified at the time of the Jewish Passover, as the Gospels tell us. Agreed?

SECOND: we know how the Jews calculated their Passover. It was always in the middle of their first month of spring. They waited until they saw the first sign of the first new moon in the spring and then they counted 14 days. That would be the full moon and that was when the Jews kept the Passover.

THIRD: the first Christians also kept Easter at the time of the Jewish Passover.

FOURTH: but Easter is the great festival of the Resurrection.

61

We know that Christ rose from the dead on a Sunday, 'the first day of the week'. So Christians began to think that Easter should always be on a Sunday. Of course Passover could be on any day of the week, because it was always the 14th day (or really night) of the moon-month. A few Christians did continue to keep Easter on the 14th day, whatever day of the week that was, and the rest of the Church got very cross with them.

FIFTH: what about those years when the 14th day of the moon-month was in fact a Sunday? Was it right for the great Christian festival to be held on the same day as the Jewish Passover? Some Christians, including our Irish, thought 'yes'. But in time the great majority thought 'no'. So if the 14th day of the moon-month was a Sunday those Christians would prefer to celebrate Easter the following Sunday, which would be the 21st day of the moon-month.

Are you awake, brother? Pangur has gone to sleep.

SIXTH: to summarise. Some Christians, including our Irish, celebrated Easter on the Sunday in the week from the 14th to the 20th day of the moon-month. Other celebrated it on the Sunday in the week from the 15th to the 21st day.

SEVENTH: but which month are we talking about? It had to be the first month of spring. When does spring begin? Well, it is obvious to us who live here that in summer the days are very long and the winter nights are very long. But there is one day in spring and one day in autumn when the days and the nights are the same length. That day in spring is the important day. We can't celebrate Easter before then.

EIGHTH: to summarise again. Easter is the first Sunday after the first full moon after the equal-day-night in spring. That's how it's now decided, brother.

NINTH: but how do you know in advance when that is going to be? You have to know in advance. Otherwise you wouldn't know when to start Lent. Here I can only tell you that very clever men have puzzled over this and some of them have made sort-of charts to work out when Easter will be. But very clever men don't always agree with each other, so their charts don't always agree either. Our Irish teachers used one chart but at Rome they used a newer one which they said was better.

TENTH: to summarise finally. So the problem for us was partly that our Irish teachers were content to keep Easter on the 14th day of the moon-month if that was a Sunday, and also that the chart used by the Irish was different from the one used in Rome. In many years it made no difference. But it could happen that in some years the Christians of the Iona 'empire' would keep Easter a whole week before Christians from Rome and other countries.

It's a relief to have got to the end of that. I had to count it out on my fingers as that was the only way I could learn it. It made me feel good to see that the 10th finger and the 10th point were coming up at the same time.

So now wake up again and I'll tell you how the matter became so important to us.

King Oswiu's queen, Eanflaed, was the daughter of King Edwin. So she was Northumbrian born and she was in fact the very first Christian to be baptised by Paulinus in his mission to the north. Of course it was her father who decided that she should be baptised, as a sort of halfway stage on his own journey towards the Christian faith; she was just a new-born infant at the time. When her father King Edwin was killed in battle her mother, Queen Ethelburga, decided to return to Kent where she came from. So Eanflaed was brought up in Kent and was naturally trained in the Roman customs of the missionaries in Kent. Her husband-to-be, Oswiu, kept to the customs of Iona. When they were married this meant that, some years, Oswiu would be feasting and keeping Easter while his queen was still fasting and keeping Lent. This might not have mattered, as kings and queens don't have to eat every meal together: they have plenty of space. But the King's son, Ahlfrith, made it known that he too favoured Roman ways. So perhaps Oswiu felt a bit pressurised.

The first thing we knew here of the change to come was one day when Bishop Colman gathered us together and told us that the King had asked him and some of the senior monks to go to a meeting at Abbess Hild's monastery at Whitby. The King had become concerned about the disagreements among Christians. For himself, the King said, he had always been quite satisfied with the ways of Iona. But it ought to be decided. So the King invited Lindisfarne to speak in defence of its customs, and there would be a speaker (Colman did not know who) putting the other side.

King Oswiu had always supported us well enough, but this left us feeling uneasy. As Colman said, we didn't want to dictate to any other Christians; we just wanted to go on doing what we had learned from those who founded our church. Yet clearly there could be a problem if Christians kept Easter on different dates. There were other things as well. The other Christians did not like our tonsure. Their monks all wore the crown-of-thorns tonsure which you and I now wear, John. But in those days we all wore the Irish tonsure: shaved at the front and long at the back. The other Christians called us 'pagan druids'. So what? I can almost hear my grandfather's voices saying, 'There was a lot of good in druids'. Our tonsure served its purpose; it meant that everyone we met knew what we were: men of religion, monks. It didn't seem credible that Christians should quarrel over a thing like that.

Still, there was an air of foreboding over the monastery from the time our bishop told us about that meeting. On the day our representatives left, by boat of course, we were a subdued group of brothers who went to wave them off.

On the day they were expected back we scanned the horizon until we saw the boat. I'm not fey, John, but I declare there was something about the appearance of the boat in the distance. As soon as we could see their figures we knew they were dejected. Immediately they disembarked Bishop Colman told us, briefly but with dignity, that they had been unsuccessful. He said that they would have food and brief rest, then he would call us together to tell us what had happened.

We gathered for that meeting sick at heart. Colman told us, "The King summoned the meeting and took his seat. We looked across to see who was there. I was most interested to see a very aged man, over eighty I should think, who I was told was Deacon James. I had heard about him: he had come up north with Paulinus and Queen Ethelburga; he worked with Paulinus. When Paulinus fled, after the death of Edwin, James stayed and continued all these years to do valiant Christian work in the area of York. It was good to see Bishop Cedd. (I jumped at that, John. Of course I knew that Cedd was a bishop. But I thought of him really as still one of us boys in the school.) Cedd was acting as interpreter to make sure there were no misunderstandings because of language difficulties. Of course we couldn't speak in Latin because the King doesn't understand it. I felt sure that Cedd would be a wise and balanced presence there.

"Then we saw that there was an elderly bishop, whom we assumed would be the chief speaker on the other side, and sitting next to him, to our surprise, Wilfrid!"

"Wilfrid!" we all exclaimed.

"None other," said Colman. "Of course we knew that Wilfrid had spent several years in study at Rome after he left us. We knew that he was friendly with the King's son, Ahlfrith, and had founded a monastery at Ripon after the Melrose monks left there. But," said Colman, "I can't say that I really thought that he would take sides against us. But he did. The chief speaker on the other side was not the elderly bishop I mentioned, but Wilfrid."

There was silence. I think we were all remembering Wilfrid as we had known him as a boy among us.

Colman went on, "He spoke extremely well, and I'm sure he believed every word he said. I am sure that his years of study at Rome have given him a real love for things Roman and he feels, like a missionary, that he must give this to the world. It may be that he has forgotten his debt to us and the love he used to have. Or it may be that he feels that his love for us can best be expressed by bringing us into Roman ways."

I thought then, brother, what a good man Colman was! As for me, if I could have got my hands on Wilfrid at that moment I would have expressed my feelings for him quite differently!

"How did the debate go, Father?" asked one of the brothers.

"There was all the usual argument about the date of Easter. We're quite familiar with that. Both sides quoted the authorities on which they based their position. I was not angry with what Wilfrid said until he referred to us as just a tiny group of Christians on the extreme edge of the world: as if that made our opinions of no account. But we were clearly out-argued and I could see which way the debate was going. Yet the King's final remark before he gave his decision took me by surprise. Wilfrid had based a lot of what he said on the authority of Saint Peter. I had quoted Saint John. Then Wilfrid said it was Peter who had the keys to the Kingdom. King Oswiu turned to me. "Is that true, Colman?" he asked. "Yes," I replied, as of course I had to. "Does Saint John have such power?" he asked. "No," I said. "Then," said the King, "because I don't want to be turned away when I arrive at the gates of heaven I declare for Saint Peter." He said it with a slight, grim, twisted smile. Then I got up, bowed to the King, and came away with the rest of the brothers. What stunned me most in that moment was that the decision had turned, not on Easter and so on, but on the personal fate of the King. But when we had time to gather our thoughts of course we felt terrible. Those of us who are Irish came here leaving everything and at the risk of our lives. We were the pioneers here; and now we were rejected.

"But, brothers, we won't wallow in emotion and you've heard enough for now. I want everyone to be clear about this, though, that there will be no place in Oswiu's kingdom for those who will not accept his decision. Now let us separate and tomorrow we will meet and think again."

So the meeting broke up and immediately there was confusion: everyone wanted to put his feeling into words. But I wasn't very good at that, John, and I do so hate disagreements. So as soon as I could I escaped to find Pangur. As I hugged him I realised that there was no choice for me. I would stay here.

It was a relief when the bell summoned us to night prayers and to silence; not that many of us slept much that night. The next day Bishop Colman held the meeting early. He said, "Each of you is free to decide. I do not claim the obedience of any monk. I and the Irish monks, who came from Iona, have decided that we shall leave, return to Iona first, and then perhaps to another monastery elsewhere in Ireland. If any of the English monks wish to accompany us you are very welcome. We shall live together according to the traditions we have so far followed. To those English monks who wish to stay here I would say, "Don't think that we in any way condemn you or think you disloyal. This is a time of very confused loyalties. Those of you who stay here will stay with our blessing. We hope that those of us who go will go with your blessing, and that we shall all pray for each other in the years ahead."

I thought again, what a good man he was. He did not complain or criticize. And quite a lot of the English monks did decide to go with him. The day they went was one of the worst days of my life. We felt as if someone had given us two cuts with a scythe: the first cut had taken off our Irish leaders, and the next had divided the English monks in two. There were enough of those who stayed to form a monastery, but what a contrast! It was a baffled and bedraggled little monastery that was left behind.

Did we ever hear of them again? Well yes, brother, we did. News does travel. One of my particular friends who decided to go (much younger than me) was called Gerald. He had been one of the most promising boys in the school here, and it was through him that we heard what happened next.

First they went to Iona and broke the news to them. But it was never planned that they should stay there and Colman wanted to found his own monastery. So they all moved to an island called Inishboffin. But then the English and the Irish quarrelled. Gerald told me that in the Spring the Irish monks suddenly said that they felt called to go on a prolonged mission, so they went. So the English, whether they felt called to it or not, had to stay, work in the fields and prepare the harvest. Then, just as they finished getting in the harvest, all the Irish monks turned up again, to settle for the winter and of course eat and drink and so on. The English didn't like it. There was so much bad feeling that in the end Colman decided to start a second monastery. He left the Irish at Inishboffin and settled the English at a place called Mayo. We heard that Colman died about 10 years after leaving us, and my friend Gerald became Abbot of Mayo. The last I heard he is still there and the monastery is doing very nicely.

But, as I said, Brother John, I couldn't go. I am English, Bernician English, and every bit of me belongs here. King Oswiu was my king, whatever he said or did, and I owed him loyalty. But I puzzled over why he decided the way he did. Could he, I wondered, really be so anxious about what would happen to him at the gate of heaven? Well, I thought, yes, he could. It is a reasonable fear for anyone, for judgment is real and we shall have to answer for our deeds and the way we have spent our lives. King Oswiu had been responsible for quite a few deaths, probably even murders. There was the death of King Oswine, for instance.

As I said before, many fingers were pointed at Oswiu for involvement in that, because he wanted to join Bernicia and Deira into one kingdom, as indeed he did after Oswine died. And perhaps there was at least one other murder. I mentioned Oswiu's son, Ahlfrith. It was rumoured that he had been plotting to get the throne and that he had been pushing for the synod to happen because he counted on his father taking the Irish side, looking outdated, and being more easily disposed of. But if so his father was too crafty for him, and perhaps that was the reason for the grim smile as he made his decision. It showed that Oswiu was a king who moved with the times. He lived out his reign and died in his bed. It was his son who disappeared from history, suddenly and finally, and there were nasty rumours about that. Kings live in a violent world, John, or used to before our present king, Aldfrith. But it is quite possible, I decided, that Oswiu would need the friendship of Saint Peter when he arrived at the gate of heaven.

All that did not make him any less my king, and I knew that Colman was being realistic when he said that there would be no room in the kingdom for anyone who disagreed. My loyalty was to

Oswiu; my loyalty was also to Aidan. I wanted to stay here, where my early memories were. In this whole matter the hardest and most painful moment for me was when Bishop Colman decided to open Aidan's grave, to take back some of Aidan's bones to Iona with them. I knew that this was right and proper and important for them, but I could hardly bear to stand there and see Aidan's remains disturbed. Yet to me Aidan is not bones in a grave. To this day he is a living presence. I half expect, still, to see him round every corner.

This is his monastery, and here I shall stay.

I'm sure all this story of conflict, John, seems to you very remote. I don't think those of us English monks who stayed could ever feel quite as passionately about it as the Irish did. As I said, this country had been part of the Roman Empire and we English came from the continent not so very long ago. The continent couldn't be all that bad, and there was a lot to be said for Christian peace and unity. So I thought, and so did some of the others. So we grew our hair and were re-tonsured in the crown-of-thorns style, and waited to see what would happen next.

But of course we couldn't live without a leader, and that is the next bit of my story.

CHAPTER 8   CUTHBERT AS PRIOR

So we had had three Irish bishops one after the other, John, and it was natural to suppose that our next bishop would be Irish also. But there was a difference. Bishop Tuda didn't come from Iona but from south Ireland. He had already been consecrated as he was on the spot and available when Colman left. But he wasn't our bishop for long. The year of King Oswiu's synod was a very bad year for plague. Hardly had Bishop Tuda been appointed than he caught the plague and died. So he had no time really to do anything and after his death no bishop was appointed to Lindisfarne for quite a long time.

But now I look back on it from my old age I can see that Bishop Tuda did do something for me. You remember, brother that Colman rightly said there would be no place in this kingdom for anyone who did not accept the decision of King Oswiu's synod. But Tuda had no problem, because he had, in a way, already accepted it in advance. It became clear that in southern Ireland where he came from the Irish had already decided to calculate the date of Easter as they did at Rome, to wear the crown-of-thorns tonsure, and so on. Tuda would have been an excellent person to help us to accept what had happened, if he had not died. At least he made me see that my outlook had been too limited. Somehow I had supposed that all the Irish thought the same way as our Irish. So to me the synod had been a kind of contest: the Irish on one side, and on the other side those who came from Rome, who loved Rome, or who thought Rome was right. I had thought it was a kind of battle: the Irish against the Romans.

But Tuda helped me to see that it was not so. On the date-of-Easter question and the other matters discussed at the synod many of the Irish – who were just as Irish as our Irish – had already accepted the Roman position and found no problem in it. I even brought myself to think that perhaps one day Iona will accept it as well.

For me this altered things. I didn't feel so bad about the decision of the synod. It was in any case a decision I couldn't escape as I knew I couldn't leave. But Tuda helped me to live with it.

We were still trying to recover from all these changes when we had another blow: the death of Cedd.

You remember that he had been one of my friends in school here. As Chad's oldest brother he was rather dignified and I suppose I never knew him really well. But we kept track of the work he did when he left Lindisfarne. As a missionary priest, and then bishop, he did exactly the sort of work Aidan had hoped his pupils would grow up to do. As I mentioned before, Cedd was one of the small pioneer team to go to the Middle Angles after Peada was baptised. Then he was recalled from there to be the head of the mission to the East Saxons; then he became their bishop. But he never forgot Northumbria, nor did Northumbria forget him. Now, a bit of history! After King Oswiu was killed in battle his son reigned for a little while as King of Deira. He decided he would like to found a new monastery. It seems he wanted it as somewhere he could go and pray, and also where he could be buried when he died. So Ethelwald consulted his chaplain, who was none other than another of our schoolmates and another of Cedd's brothers, Caelin. Caelin introduced Cedd to King Ethelwald; Cedd was asked to choose the place for the monastery, and he chose the place we now call Lastingham. He had to choose carefully. On the one hand it mustn't be so remote that no one could get to it. That would have been stupid, but there was a good road not too far from the place that Cedd chose. But the King didn't want it in a town or a village. He wanted it to be a little apart. And Cedd, like the Irish monks who trained us, was always a bit fascinated by the idea of the wilderness, the desert place, which the Bible said was the haunt of demons as well as wild animals. The bravest of us always wanted to fight demons.

Not me, brother! I like living among people, and cats! I don't mind if I never meet a demon. Pangur! Stop clawing at me and gazing at me with those wild yellow eyes of yours!

So Cedd chose his site; then he had to purify it. This was what our Irish teachers always said before anyone began building a new monastery: the place must be cleansed to drive away the demons and to wash away any stain of old crimes committed in or near that place. Cedd decided to spend the whole of Lent there, 40 days, fasting and praying. By 'fasting' I understand that he just took a little food each evening: some bread, some milk and an egg. That was all he ate, every day except Sundays. He prayed, meditated and slept at the site. But just 10 days before the end of Lent the King asked Cedd to go to him, so Cedd whistled up another of his brothers and asked him to complete the fast. It seems it doesn't matter who fights the demons as long as someone does. Then the monastery was built.

Well, so far as I know, Cedd went back to the East Saxons until he turned up at King Oswiu's synod to be the interpreter. From there I suppose he went straight back to Lastingham and there caught the plague and died. His youngest brother, my friend Chad, had now come back from Ireland and Cedd, with his last breath, asked him to look after Lastingham. So Chad became Abbot there.

That year was a bad year in a number of ways, not just for us here at Lindisfarne but for everyone. It was a bad year for plague. Cedd died of it; Tuda died of it; so did hundreds of others. Plague is terrifying; it's so sudden. People died within a few days or sometimes even a few hours. Our Irish teachers used to tell us that all good monks, indeed all good Christians, should live prepared for death at any moment. Plague certainly underlined that message. Later Cuthbert told us about the plague at Melrose in which his friend Boisil died and he himself caught it and recovered. Just a few years ago I met a young monk of Jarrow, called Bede, who told me that plague almost wiped out his community when he was a boy. We've had plague at Lindisfarne too, John, and many brothers died. I didn't get it myself, but it was just horrifying to live with friends collapsing on all sides. There must be a cause for it. Some people say it's a punishment sent by God. Some of the monks here, when we got it at Lindisfarne, said that it was because there was too much light-heartedness in our community, including too much enjoyment of the old pagan stories. They said that Cuthbert himself, who was a hermit at the time, had warned them. But I don't know, brother. I'm not clever enough to know about that kind of thing. Sometimes I sit and wonder whether God, who is so loving, would do a thing like that. I know parts of the Bible say he does, but I still wonder.

It's an old man's privilege to sit and think funny thoughts.

However, that's brought us onto the next stage in our story, John. The time has come to introduce your particular hero, Cuthbert.

I don't really know what would have happened to us after Tuda's death if the King had not remembered and acted on the last piece of advice Bishop Colman gave him before he left. "Get Eata of Melrose to look after Lindisfarne," he said. Eata! That was good news. You remember that he had been one of the first boys in the school here, senior to me, and I knew he was a serious and well-organised person. I thought, "If anyone can get us up and running again it will be Eata." But then a further surprise and, at first, a disappointment. Although Eata did indeed come and visit us, several times, in the end he asked someone else to be actually in charge of our day-to-day recovery. That someone was his prior, Cuthbert, whom none of us really knew. As far as I know Cuthbert had never been to Lindisfarne before the day when he came, so to speak, to take over.

The next few weeks – or was it even months? – were pretty tough on everyone. Naturally we Lindisfarne monks were still stunned and very miserable. Some of us even went into depression and stayed there. Petty little quarrels between brothers, which had been held in check in the earlier years when we were so full of our life and mission, broke out and filled some people's minds. One or two tried to assert a sort of leadership and found themselves rejected by the rest.

I can see now that it needed someone from outside to sort us out. But even the fact that it was someone from outside was resented at first. After all, Lindisfarne was the mother of Melrose and was Melrose now going to order us around?

I did what I always do when there's trouble, brother. I retreated into the background and kept quiet and just watched and listened. But I thought, "This Cuthbert is going to have a hard time." I just hoped he would be a strong enough man to cope.

Well, he came. He was at least physically big and strong (though not as big and strong as I was in those days). He looked like a man who knew his own mind, but who liked to be friendly with people and was naturally cheerful. But that didn't melt some of our brothers and so Cuthbert really did have to show that he was in charge.

This is how he did it. I think he had made a firm resolution in his mind never to quarrel with us. Every day he held a meeting of the brothers, at which naturally he was chairman. He always came in smiling pleasantly and began to explain his ideas for the smooth running of the monastery. And as always, as soon as he stopped speaking, opposition broke out. "We don't want this… we don't like that… we are not used to the other… Aidan said… Finan said… Colman said…" Well, they could have gone with Colman if they'd wanted to, but Cuthbert never threw that at them. Occasionally I tried to put in a word to help, but I didn't say much. I'm not the sort of person who can think of solutions to problems when no one else can. I get very confused when ideas, not to say insults, are flying around. But each day, when it became clear that the meeting was not going to get any further, Cuthbert ended it by smiling pleasantly and walking out. At the next meeting he would begin as if nothing had gone wrong the time before.

I can't tell you how long this went on. It seemed endless while it was happening. The tension in the monastery was incredible. Then, quite suddenly, the opposition gave way. That was helped by the deaths of one or two of the older brothers. God forbid that I should ever wish anyone dead! But I'm trying to tell you the story honestly as it happened, and there's no denying the fact that these deaths did help. And suddenly we were through the worst and Cuthbert was really running the monastery and we were holding up our heads again and looking to the future.

Cuthbert was a good leader. I couldn't feel for him what I felt for Aidan, though I came to admire him too. His standards were quite strict but he always worked hard himself at the jobs he asked others to do, even the rough physical work, which he actually seemed to enjoy. I don't know why I should be surprised about that; people with muscles like to use them, as I ought to know. It became clear too that he had a naturally happy temperament and liked to be easy and friendly with everyone. Like Aidan he continued to be a missionary and an enterprising one too. Sometimes he was away from the monastery for a whole month at a time. We heard that he used to penetrate into parts of mountain or forest land where no Christian missionary had been before, always looking for people who had not yet heard the Christian faith. He never asked me to go on these journeys, though he did not usually go alone. He preferred to take one or more of the younger monks with him, to give them experience and training. So I have no real first-hand knowledge of Cuthbert as a missionary at this stage. Later, as I will tell you, he did take me with him on some expeditions.

The biggest change Cuthbert brought to the monastery was through his gift of healing. You, John, of course have the best of reasons for knowing that this gift was real. I never had any reason to doubt it, though I had to suppress a pang of jealousy on Aidan's behalf, who didn't have this gift, when the whole world began to come here seeking help from Cuthbert. That's how it felt. I suppose it must have started gradually with him, with one or two remarkable cures when he prayed or laid hands on the sick. But when people discovered how compassionate he was (and he genuinely was) they began to bring all their troubles to him – illness of body or mind, sad hearts or loaded consciences. I couldn't help being glad for the people, when you saw them arrive tired, worried or in pain, and then go home happy, thankful and relived. As I said before, our monastery was always open to people and we always had had lots of guests. Now we just had a lot more!

But it did change our way of life. Cuthbert became very popular and people like to show their gratitude. Of course we never asked anyone to pay for healing. But we accepted gifts from those in a position to give us something. A monastery does need resources in order to survive. In all sorts of ways these were flourishing and expansive years. Our scriptorium had begun to develop and making books is very costly. We did try to preserve our simple lifestyle. We were aware of the dangers of becoming popular and rich! I remember with a touch of heartache how Aidan rigorously gave away anything we were given beyond our actual needs, to keep us both hardy and dependent on God.

But those days were good years, though for me marred by one piece of bad news. I was in my middle forties, and as strong and fit as ever, when we heard of the death of my dearest boyhood friend, Chad. The last thing I told you about Chad was that he had become Abbot of Lastingham. But those of us who knew Chad always supposed he would be a bishop one day. He was so clever and so good; and, of course, since his years in Ireland he was very highly educated in the Irish fashion. So we were delighted when we heard that the King had asked him to be a bishop at York. But sometime later Wilfrid reappeared on the scene. He had gone abroad after the King's synod, but now he claimed that he had previously been asked to be bishop of York. There was a real muddle, brother, and I'm sure that none of us here really understood it. Archbishop Theodore came up from Canterbury to sort it out. Of course Wilfrid was, like Chad, very clever, and also highly educated, though in the Roman fashion. In the end the Archbishop asked Chad to step down. He did this very gracefully, saying that he had never deserved to be a bishop anyway. Then he went back to Lastingham.

But not for long. The Archbishop was impressed by Chad's goodness, which shone out of the whole affair. He still wanted Chad to be a bishop, but somewhere else. He had some doubts about whether Chad had been properly consecrated when he was first made bishop, so he re-consecrated him himself, just to make sure. Then he asked Chad to go to Mercia to do pioneering missionary work there.

I never saw him again. The messenger who brought us the news of his death told us some of the stories current in his monastery. One was that he was warned of his death beforehand, by angels who came with heavenly music to tell him of it. Another was that at the moment of his death it was not simply angels but his brother Cedd who came to escort him to heaven. Even in my grief I had to laugh at that, John. I thought, "How like Cedd! Always the one to order his brothers about and be responsible for them. It would be just like him to fetch Chad!" but my sense of loss was very great. I think, of all Aidan's disciples, Chad was most like Aidan.

He was the first real friend of my boyhood and this life seemed bleaker without him.

But, as I said, those were good years. I continued my work as an ordinary monk: some share in the farming and fishing, some work in the kitchens and guest-house, some travelling on the mainland as part of a mission team, and the daily round of worship. I continued to sing well, to my delight and, although I say it, to the delight of others. And there was always Pangur for solace. I felt I had reached my limits.

I've told you, Brother John, what Cuthbert was like when he was here as prior: busy, active, firm, cheerful, friendly. When it was known on the mainland that he had the gift of healing large numbers of people came to see him. He seems to have done something for most of them and at least sent them away happier. This was work he loved. You could see and feel that there was something in him deeply satisfied.

But after some years, eight or nine I think, a change came over him. We all felt it. He was quieter. Sometimes he would stop in the middle of doing a job, as if he had to pause and think. Sometimes you would catch him doing nothing, just standing there gazing out to sea. It wasn't like him. He liked to get on with things and get them done.

Then, one day at the meeting, he told us. "I think," he said, "that God is calling me to go away and become a hermit." We were thunderstruck. Of course we knew that the life of prayer meant everything to him: it was vital. But so it was to Aidan and others of the brothers and they never became hermits. They went into retreat for a while but always came back. And Cuthbert at his best was a really sociable man; he really loved people; and he had this mysterious gift of healing. Why should he of all people be called to go off alone?

When I heard about it I also needed to go off for a bit, to stump round the island and puzzle it out.

Pangur was no use at all to me at this moment.

Although I told him all about it he seemed to say he couldn't see any problem; he often needed to be alone and to prove it he left me and went hunting. So I was left with my own thoughts and with the talk that was going on all round the monastery.

Of course I knew that if God really called us, whatever he called us to do, we had to obey. Aidan had said that; all the monks knew that; we prayed all the time that God's will be done. But why had this happened? Why did God will this? You know that I'm not very clear-headed and easily muddled in an argument, but I could have explained to anyone what monks were for. But what were hermits for?

Fortunately some of our brothers knew the answer better than I did and this was the kind of answer I got:

You know how difficult it sometimes is to do the right thing, and we have to struggle with temptation? You know how we read in the Bible about the forces of evil, called Satan and the demons, who fight against God and try to spoil his creation? And you know that there is a spiritual war going on, good against evil, and we are called to fight on the side of good? Well, to be a hermit is not a rest-cure! If God calls anyone to be a hermit then God calls him into the thick of that battle. He is to be a front-line soldier. By prayer and discipline he fights against evil, relying on the grace of God only, and on no human help. To be a faithful hermit is to do the hardest job of all and the most important.

But, I said, what about all his healings? What about his missionary work? What about running this monastery? Aren't these important? What good will other people get if he goes off to be a hermit? And the answer I got was:

Brother, there is only one thing important in life and that is doing God's will. The life of prayer is supremely important and God calls some to give themselves totally to it. You ask, what good do others get? Brother, remember that spiritually we are all one in the Body of Christ. Cuthbert's obedience, Cuthbert's faithfulness, will bring great good to us all: not just to us monks but to all Christians. If he is truly called he will do more good alone as a hermit than he might by even a large number of healings, for his victory will be victory for us all.

That was the kind of thinking and talking that was going on in the monastery.

One day soon afterwards Cuthbert spoke to us again. He said, "I must try this vocation. It won't go away. So I need somewhere to test it out. I intend to go just a little way from the monastery.

I'll live in a hut on the tiny island just there, the one off the tip of Lindisfarne."

So he lived there for a little while. I won't presume to say what his inner experience was. But outwardly it wasn't much like being a hermit. For one thing he could see and hear us all the time as we went about our work. At any time, at low tide, he could have walked back and joined us. Also, people still wanted to get to him and be healed. Of course they did. And of course Cuthbert was still the same friendly, helpful person he had always been. But it was clear that it wasn't satisfying him.

So he came back and asked us all to meet him. He said, "That was a kind of experiment but I must go further away. I have decided to go and be a hermit on the Farne Island." The Farne! There was a murmur through the group. Some brothers looked at him almost in horror. He saw their expression and smiled, a bit grimly I thought. "I know what you're thinking. The Farne is haunted, devil possessed. No one has ever stayed there alone except Aidan. Even sailors and fishermen dread having to land there. But, brothers, if I am to fight the demons I must go where the demons are!" Then he smiled again, a bit more relaxed. "In any case, brothers, I've got to eat. Do you know any other island round here where food can be grown?" We didn't, of course. We all knew that the rest of the islands in that group were bare rock: the home of seals and kittiwakes, but not hermits.

So it was settled and he prepared to go. But a hermitage had to be built there and he was willing to accept help in building it. I, among others, volunteered. So the day came when, with a calm sea and a good wind, Cuthbert and a group of us set sail for the Farne.

None of us had ever been there before, and our stomachs churned as we approached. I gathered strength from the fact that Aidan used to go there on retreat sometimes, and to my mind Aidan was a match for any demon. I recalled one story about Aidan and the Farne, which I'll tell you, brother, if I may. This story filled my mind as we landed and walked round, and particularly when we realised how clearly we could see Bamburgh, castle and town.

I've mentioned already a certain King of Mercia, called Penda, who was a very good fighter. He was the king who killed Oswald and was eventually killed by Oswiu. He was a pagan, and in my younger days in the monastery he was a kind of Big Bad Wolf to us. We boys were half-scared that he would appear out of nowhere and finish us off. Once when Aidan was in retreat on the Farne, looking towards Bamburgh, Penda and his men did appear. They had our king and the people of Bamburgh penned up in the little wooden town; they had pulled down some of the cottages on the outskirts and they were building a firewall round Bamburgh. The wind was blowing from the west, as it usually does. Once the fire was lit there would be no escape for the Northumbrians. Aidan could see all this from his island, and what could he do? He prayed. "Lord, see what evil Penda is doing." Just that, and nothing else.

Don't you think, brother, that that was quite an amazing prayer in the circumstances? I think that if I had been Aidan I'd have wanted to jump up and down, scream curses on the enemy and call down fire from heaven upon them. But not Aidan. God is God and he must be allowed to deal with the situation as it is, and as he wishes. God did deal with it. The wind changed, the smoke was blown back at the besiegers who raised the siege and went home – and, for that day, all was saved.

Whether the Farne Islands was really full of demons or not I'm not able to say. Demons don't trouble to make themselves known to ordinary folk like me, and I absolutely don't want them to. They didn't prevent our building Cuthbert's hermitage. He wanted a living hut and chapel and a high wall round them both. He explained, "When I'm in the hermitage I don't want to be distracted by the view." At first there didn't appear to be a source of fresh water and that would have been a real problem. I don't know how Aidan managed. But Cuthbert prayed and we found a spring. Cuthbert was like that! When he seemed to have all that he wanted we left him.

Obviously we intended to go back to him and to go back often. He expected to grow some of his own food, and of course he was expert at fasting and didn't need much. But we weren't going to let him die of starvation, or of anything else if we could help it: he was one of us. But it soon became clear that other people didn't intend to let him die of starvation, either. People still wanted to be healed; Cuthbert still had the gift of healing and was still as friendly and compassionate as he had always been. So they went out to him by boat. People don't take money to a hermit: they take food. So many went that Cuthbert actually made a landing-place for them, with a small guest-house near it. All the same, you know what the seas are like round here. There were days, even weeks, when no-one could go over and Cuthbert had all the solitude he wanted.

So it went on for about 10 years. As far as I know he didn't leave his island in that time. Here on Lindisfarne we were always aware of him. On bright days we would look across and almost imagine we could see him. On foggy days we would think of him completely alone in his blanket of white mist. Sometimes on a wild night in winter I would lie awake and wonder how he was feeling: alone, with the sea roaring and the wind howling and the sea-birds shrieking. Alone, with God, but no possibility of human help. To grow old and to die there, alone.

But, as you know, it didn't happen like that. Something else happened instead. At the end of 10 years as a hermit Cuthbert was called to be a bishop! Of course I don't know how it was decided: I don't sit in the councils of the great. But I do know that one day King Edgfrith, Bishop Trumwine and others went over to the Farne and asked Cuthbert to leave the hermitage and come and be a bishop. I suppose they found him in the company of the eider ducks as usual: he was particularly fond of them. Rumour says that Cuthbert wasn't at all happy at the thought of being a bishop. He wanted to stay a hermit. But if he had to be a bishop he wanted to be a bishop of Lindisfarne. I heard that they had offered him Hexham and Eata at this time had Lindisfarne. But Eata kindly agreed to take Hexham instead and then Cuthbert consented. So he was consecrated at York and returned to us as bishop.

I said he returned to us, but really we didn't see a great deal of him once he was bishop. Looking back at it from the angle of my long life, brother, his time as bishop was short: not quite two years I'd say. But he was very active and packed a lot in. Like Aidan he travelled a great deal seeking out those who had not yet heard of the Christian faith, and like Aidan he normally went on foot. Everywhere he went there were accounts of people being healed by his amazing insight and inexplicable powers. He was a very dramatic man.

On one of his journeys he asked me to go with him, and this was very exciting for me. By this time I was beginning to suspect that he was not well, though he was younger than I. I carried most of our baggage – not that we took much. We were going to a town right over on the other side of the country, called Carlisle. We made our way southwards until we came to the Roman Wall and to the river beyond it. Then we turned westwards and followed the road to Carlisle. I had never seen a Roman town before and, although I had seen something of what the Romans could do when they built the Wall, in the town my eyes were popping out. Were they giants who put up these great stone buildings?

Two things I shall never forget. We travelled around that countryside quite a bit, doing missionary work, and one day we journeyed to the edge of a lake. We looked over to a little island in the middle. Cuthbert told me that a friend of his, called Herebert, was a hermit there. They used to meet once a year, he said, and usually his friend came over to the east coast to meet him, but this year they would meet in Carlisle. So his friend came. I don't know what they said, of course. I kept in the background while they were talking. But when Cuthbert came away he looked unusually sombre, and I didn't speak to him for a while. I think he could have known that he wouldn't see that friend again. To my surprise I later heard that the friend had died on the very same day as Cuthbert himself, but I don't know if that is true.

The other thing that stays in my memory was quite shattering. One day we were walking through the town of Carlisle and as usual looking at the ruins. Indeed that day we had a town official proudly pointing them out to us. Cuthbert suddenly stopped in his tracks and said, "Oh!" Just that, nothing more. He suddenly looked paler and more gaunt than ever. Then he said, "I must go to the Queen." She was in Carlisle at the time too, while her husband King Edgfrith was fighting up in Pictland. As we stared at Cuthbert he said, "The King has just been killed and the English army massacred." Brother, my spine turned to ice: not simply at the news which was bad enough. But it was spooky: how did he know that? But he did go to the Queen; he had to tell her; and time proved that he was right. It seems that the King had been lured by the Picts much too far north, into the mountains, and then they turned on the English and wiped them out. That King was too brave for his own good.

I was quite glad to get home to Lindisfarne after that expedition, John. I have never been a very brave and adventurous man. You remember I told you how, when I was a child, the stories of Columba's strange powers frightened me? Cuthbert had similar powers. He could foretell what would happen in the future, or sometimes he knew what was happening at that time but a long way away. Those things worried me more than his powers of healing, which were always used for good. I revered him and I know that he was an exceptionally kind and loving man. But I was never quite comfortable with him. So I came back to Lindisfarne and to Pangur, and Cuthbert continued his work as a bishop almost up to the season of Christmas.

When Cuthbert came back to the monastery here, that last Christmas, we could all see the change in him. He was even thinner than before, his colour was high; his eyes were bright but not healthily bright. In private we looked at each other with foreboding, but no one knew what to say. We kept Christmas quite soberly. Cuthbert wanted it that way, and we hadn't got much heart to be merry. Finally he broke the tension himself. "I know that I can't work any longer as bishop," he said. "I know that I am going to die quite soon. I want to die in my hermitage. So I am going there now." Someone blurted out, "When shall we see you again, Father?" It was a rather stupid thing to say, but somebody had to say something. Cuthbert replied, "Probably not till you bring back my body here for burial." Then he got into his boat and went.

Of course we didn't just abandon him. Monks went out from time to time, to take food and see how he was. About the middle of March we had an anxious time, because for days the sea was too rough to go. Then, when it calmed down, some of us prepared to go over, led by Herefrith. I don't think I wanted to go, but in any case I wasn't asked to; I was given a different job. "If he dies at night," said Herefrith, "one of us will go up to the highest point on the Farne and wave two torches." As I no longer did any heavy work during the day I was asked to be the lookout. So, each night at dusk, I took Pangur and came up to the Heugh, and waited. I didn't have to wait many nights before I saw it: two tiny points of light, waving through the darkness. So I came down and told the brothers that Cuthbert was dead. The next day we brought his body back here and buried it beside the altar in Saint Peter's Church.

Herefrith told us what it had been like. "We went there in dread," he said. "We half expected to find him dead already. We found him immediately, still alive though only just; he was lying not in the hermitage but down by the landing-place. In his hand were five raw onions and he had gnawed away half of one. I think that was all the food he had had for days. But we helped him to revive a little and he was able to speak to us. He told us that he really wanted to be buried there on the Farne, but he gave in when we begged to be allowed to take his body back to Lindisfarne. He knew already that we would want that, but he had wanted to spare us all the fuss and trouble of a cult. Of course he could foresee that there would be a cult; he knew the immense reverence people already had for him. But he simply asked that in his burial we should wrap his body in the special cloth the Abbess Verca had given him. After that he spoke only of the spiritual struggle he had had, which had been intense in the last few days, and he urged our community to live in devotion and peace."

Then, as I said, brother, his body was brought back here and buried. But people could not believe that was the end of Cuthbert and so, in small numbers, they came over to pray at his tomb. I don't know quite what they expected or hoped for, but I do know what some of them claimed they got. Miracles of healing! This of course is where you first come into the story, Brother John, for you were one of those healed. I don't for a moment doubt the reality of the healings. But what did they mean? A living Christian who does healing has a special gift from God. But a dead Christian who does healings? There is only one explanation; he must be a saint in heaven!

I don't know who first made the suggestion but, once made, it grew and grew.

We have a saint!

Let's tell the world we have a saint!

Let's make it easy for people to come here and get miracles!

Let's make it easy for people to be close to the relics!

Hurrah for Saint Cuthbert of Lindisfarne!

Chapter 10   Elevation

I will say frankly to you, Brother John, that at first I wasn't completely happy at all the talk about 'elevating' Cuthbert's remains. I know that you feel differently, and so you must, since you were healed by him. I know parents are amongst his most enthusiastic devotees, and so they should be. I suppose, for myself, some of my old feelings for Aidan were getting in the way. I suppose I was a bit jealous for him. They hadn't done that for Aidan, I thought. They had allowed some of his bones to go over to Iona.

Our Bishop Eadbehrt also was hesitant. He used to talk to me sometimes. Not that I could give him advice – no one has ever asked me for advice exactly – but I would listen while he worked out his own thoughts, and he knew that I wouldn't criticise or tell anyone else. I'm only telling you because he too is dead now.

You will wonder what possible objections or hesitations there could be. Well, the bishop knew that Cuthbert himself, as he lay dying, had told Herefrith that he would prefer to be buried out there on the Farne. He had foreseen that there might be a cult if he were buried in an accessible place like Lindisfarne. It was only very reluctantly that he gave in to the wishes of the brothers about his place of burial. If Cuthbert thought like that while he was alive ought his wishes to be ignored after he was dead? I think the bishop was concerned also for the people in general and for the monastery. He didn't want to raise people's hopes in case those hopes were not met. He didn't want to saddle us with something that might be disruptive to our proper life. He knew how a cult can grow if people's enthusiasm just takes over. However, the evidence from the miracles did seem very clear and so in the end he agreed. The bishop decided that the elevation should be on March 20th, the exact anniversary of Cuthbert's death. We had to give him time to turn into a skeleton! Eleven years was thought to be the right amount of time, so we knew exactly, years in advance, when the great day would be.

During those years, as I grew older and did less heavy work in the monastery, I used to go sometimes and sit quietly in the scriptorium, watching our scribes at work. That is how I really got friendly with

Eadfrith, now our bishop, but then one of the principal scribes. He was producing beautiful texts of all kinds, handwriting so clear and even, painted work so colourful and, I thought, so different. I loved to watch him preparing his pens and inks. Finicky would be too mild a word! He was frantic about getting everything absolutely right. He would spend ages just getting his pen and ink ready. He cut his pen-nib tips to precisely the right width. Afterwards I heard someone say that his writing was so even that no one could tell where he threw away an old pen and picked up a new one. Or if he was painting he would grind the colours so fine, and mixed them carefully with white of egg. The colours really intrigued me. There were so many of them, so delicate, made from so many different things: plants, animals, rocks.

So, sometimes, Eadfrith and I would talk together, and that is how I came to know of the plan dearest to his heart: to write and illustrate a whole copy of the Gospels, making it as beautiful as he possibly could. "How many years will that take?" I asked. "Oh, a good many," he replied, "it depends on what else I have to do." "More years than I have got left?" I enquired. He was a kind man, but I could tell that he agreed.

However, he told me that he would like to think ahead and the first thing would be to go to the monastery at Jarrow, where they had a big library, and borrow the best possible text for him to copy. He then asked me whether I would like to go to Jarrow with him. I was very excited at this, as I hadn't been anywhere new for some time. I had never been to Jarrow though I knew we had friendly connections. So we got permission to go, went by boat, and spent a few days there.

There we met a young monk called Bede. I suppose he is twenty-ish and he and Eadfrith are great pals. He was very kind to me, too, and spent a lot of time with me. He seemed specially to enjoy hearing me talk about the past and he asked me a lot of questions, such as: What was Aidan like? What was Cuthbert like? What was the monastery like? Did I know King Oswald? Had I ever seen this one or that one? And so on. It is very flattering for an old man to be listened to, and I told him all I could.

"Now he'll go and write it all down," said Eadfrith after every conversation. "Why will he do that?" I asked. "It's just the way he is," said Eadfrith. "Bede has been in this monastery since he was seven. Some of the monks say that he was the most intelligent child they ever taught and absolutely thirsting for knowledge. Although he is still young he is an important teacher in the school already, and beginning to write his own textbooks. There's nothing he is not interested in. What you tell him will go down in some book or other, and one day the world will know it." "Well," I said, "I'll be astonished if the world learns anything through me. One thing I have never been is a teacher." "Wait and see," said Eadfrith. "You at your age may be able to wait and see," I said, "but as for me I shall have to watch from heaven."

But, brother, Jarrow in some ways very nearly was heaven. I saw and heard things I had never seen or heard before. Stone buildings big and solid as the rock. I just gaped when I went into the room where they keep their books. I didn't know the world had so many books. And their church! Coloured glass in the windows: glass-makers were brought over from France, I was told. Pictures on the inside walls of their church: pictures of Bible stories mainly. I could have feasted my eyes for ever. Then you should hear them sing. But this was different. And there were so many of them singing together. They told me that their first abbot, who died just a few years ago, brought a singing teacher all the way from Rome to teach them to sing the psalms the way they do. Oh, I could have stayed there a long time, just looking, just listening.

Eadfrith had been there before so this wasn't all new to him. But he was pleased with the visit: pleased when he saw my mouth opening and closing in sheer wonder and pleased that he had managed to borrow the book he wanted to copy. So we came home, guarding the precious manuscript. When we got back to Lindisfarne it did seem a bit small and plain compared with Jarrow. But it's been my home since I was a child and I soon settled back into routine. The others seemed pleased to see me back. Pangur was, for sure.

One day I was sitting watching Eadfrith in the scriptorium while he was using odd bits of parchment to try out some drawings with his big beautiful Gospels book in mind. I said, just to provoke him, "I do think your birds and dogs are a bit silly. Look at those birds! Are they ospreys or cormorants or what? Whoever saw birds with teeth? As for your dogs, what use would they be for hunting? They'd be falling over their long curly ears and long curly tails all the time. They're nothing like any dogs or birds God ever made."

Eadfrith, who is usually very good-tempered, said quite huffily, "These are my birds and dogs. God didn't make these, I did."

"Well," I said, "why is it only birds and dogs? What about this beautiful creature?" I had Pangur on my lap as I spoke.

Eadfrith laughed suddenly. "Yes," he said, "your cat is beautiful and he is very much as God made him. All right, Egfroth, your cat shall have one appearance in my book. I don't know what I'll do with his body, but he shall have your cat's head and your cat's tail." "Don't forget his whiskers," I said, "Pangur has very fine whiskers." "I'll remember to put his whiskers in," promised Eadfrith. "So be happy, Egfroth. In years to come anyone who looks at my books, and finds the right page, will see your cat."

All this thinking about reading and writing and painting, has reminded me of our present king. Aldfrith is a most remarkable man, and even more remarkable as a king. I wonder if he is the very first English king who can read and write? Usually the only place to learn these things is a monastic school and it seems that Aldfrith was educated by monks. His early years are something of a mystery. We know that he is the son of King Oswiu, but it seems not by a regular marriage. They say that his mother was an Irish princess called Fina, and his own name in Irish is Fland Fina. They say that he was brought up among the Irish. We know that he stayed out of the way while his half-brother Edgfrith was on the throne and, as I said earlier, he spent some time at Iona and knew the monks there well. Perhaps it was there, or at an earlier Irish monastery, that he learned to read and write.

Now, brother, I can read and write, but I've never been over keen on these things. But King Aldfrith really is keen. I've even heard that he can write in Irish: poetry too!

Most of the Irish monks I knew in my earlier days loved poetry. Of course kings often like poetry also, provided that it is about them and their great deeds, and provided that someone else writes it! But Aldfrith doesn't seem to be too interested in great deeds. He's certainly learned from Edgfrith's defeat by the Picts and he has made peace with them. It seems that Northumbria is quite big enough for him as it is.

I've never spoken to the King, though he has been here several times. I think he likes to go into the scriptorium and talk to the scribes and the artists. Young Bede mentioned that he visits Jarrow as well. There are enough books there to make him feel at home. Of course the books there tend to be Roman rather than Irish but perhaps the King is helping them to see some good in the culture he learned as a youth.

So, there or here, there's plenty going on for him to see and encourage. We Northerners are becoming very good at the arts of peace. Sometimes I wonder what's going to happen when there's another war, because we mustn't suppose that all the other kings in the world have become men of peace.

And sometimes I wonder what my grandfather would have thought about King Aldfrith!

So, brother, the day of the Elevation drew near. Of course it was going to be a day of great rejoicing. It's a wonderful thing for a community to be able to tell the world that one of its members is now a saint in heaven and that there are miracles of healing to prove it. So there was a lot of excitement in the monastery. I, of course, was too old to have any particular job but I was everyone's confidant and friend. It was all planned down to the last detail and, I must say, very well planned.

And yet, somehow, I didn't expect it to go off entirely peacefully. It wasn't that I was worried about the thought of seeing a skeleton. Death, bodies, and skeletons – I've seen plenty: no one who has lived to my age can escape all that. Though, having said that, I must say that there is something a little strange in seeing the skeleton of someone you have known so well in full health.

I don't know why I had this slightly uneasy feeling. I certainly wasn't prepared for what happened. The ceremony did go as planned until we got as far as bringing up the coffin and raising the lid. I was among the senior monks standing at the front. We all moved forward to look. We expected a skeleton: what we got was a whole body. There lay Cuthbert exactly as we had last seen him when we closed that coffin up eleven years before: whole, un-decayed, looking as if he was asleep. I felt shock, amazement and then a rush of something like anger. I was just about aware of the pandemonium around me. Then, for the first time in my life, I fainted.

I came round sitting down, with two of the younger monks supporting me, giving me water. But I must say the rest of that day is blotted out in my mind.

Of course there was no doubt about the meaning of it. God had worked a miracle: He has declared that Cuthbert is a great saint. In the year that has passed since then, brother, we have seen a great growth in the number of pilgrims and the number of healings. Don't misunderstand me, John. I'm delighted that you were healed and I'm delighted for everyone else who has benefited from praying at Saint Cuthbert's shrine.

It's just that there are two pictures that keep coming into my mind at the same time. One is that of us all standing there rejoicing, waiting to receive the relics of Cuthbert. The other is of thirty years earlier when we stood around, sad, fearful of the future, while Bishop Colman and our Irish monks uncovered another grave and carefully removed some of the bones – yes, bones – of Aidan.

I can't sort it out, brother. Why Cuthbert and not Aidan? What in God's eyes makes a saint? I can't sort it out, but I have my memories and I can't deny them. I shall carry the questions with me through death and into what lies beyond.

CHAPTER 11   LAST WORDS

And that, brother, bring us up to the present and to the end of my story.

The monastery has changed so much over my 62 years. It has grown so much bigger and so much wealthier. Thank God we shall cling hard to the essentials: prayer and worship, missionary work, educating the young. Each of us still lives a life of poverty and obedience. But how rich our community has become! Our church now has lead walls and roof: Bishop Eadbehrt saw to that. We have bigger buildings and far more of them. Our scriptorium is famous and also quite fantastically expensive. But we have the money, because people give it to us. Famous and wealthy people come to stay here and to die. We have lands and rich connections. It is all good, John, if only we can use it well and keep God and the Gospel in the centre. But sometimes I get afraid for the future. I know what wealth and power can do.

So I am glad that I have my memories: very clear and powerful memories; sometimes they seem to blot out the present. At times the most vivid thing to me is the picture of that first monastery: Aidan's face and voice; then the faces and voices of Chad, Cedd, Cynebil, Eata… and others. The feel and smell of our wax tablets in the school. The shouting of the boys running down to the sea to swim. The singing in the little church, and my own voice high and clear. The little wooden huts we lived in, and the wind permanently pulsating around them.

When I was a young monk, brother, I used to try to picture heaven.

We were always being told that life is a journey, so sometimes I would think of a road stretching upwards, with a great gate at the top, and angels waiting to welcome this one who was just arriving. Sometimes I would think of a great hall and a feast going on, for in the gospels there are stories of God giving a great feast. Sometimes I would just remember those moments when I was happy, and then try to think of a great happiness, more perfect, going on forever. Sometimes I would think of my friends and hope that heaven would include being with them again.

And sometimes, when I was sitting and stroking Pangur, and thinking how beautiful and loving he is, I have just known that God did not make him to throw him away.

But now that I am old I have given up thinking about the details, or trying to picture heaven. Of course I hope to meet again those I have loved, but I feel I know enough about God to trust myself to him and to trust to him all I have loved. I sit and think about the promises of the Bible that God's Kingdom will be far more wonderful than anything we can imagine here: that things that are broken will be mended and discords turned into harmony.

And it's exciting to know that for me, now, this can't be very far away. It's pleasant at the moment to be so senior in the monastery, and I realise that I have been allowed to see a stage of life most never reach. But I believe that I shall go to God soon.

We must end now, brother. Bless you for listening. And I hope indeed that you will be as truly blessed in your life in this monastery as I have been. When I think of all that God has given me I know that if I am able to choose my last thoughts my last prayer will be simply "Thank you."

DEO GRATIAS

FINIS

EPILOGUE BY BROTHER JOHN

Brother Egfroth died a few weeks after our last conversation. He died peacefully in his sleep. Pangur also was asleep on the bed at the time, and I was sitting beside him. We all went to his funeral and he was buried in the monks' graveyard here on Lindisfarne.

Brother Egfroth never had much opinion of himself and his abilities. In some ways this was realistic. Although he was a member here for 62 years he was never chosen for any position of leadership or responsibility in the monastery. That was sensible. He was not a leader and any such responsibility would have weighed him down. But he was a greater man than he would have accepted. He was essentially a straight, simple man without a touch of sophistication. He knew that he would never follow the workings of the mind of, for example, a clever man like Wilfrid. But he was utterly loyal: to the people he loved and admired, to the community here. He obeyed his abbot, kept the rules and lived the life. He did all the jobs given to him with as much competence as he had; and he grew in wisdom with the years.

When I knew him, in his old age, everybody here both respected and loved him, though it might have been hard for him to realise that. People were always the main reality to him; as he told me, he absorbed his faith from people not from books; but isn't this the way it is with most Christians?

As so it was as true of him as it was of the Apostle Paul that he "fought a good fight and finished the course." As far as I saw, no angels descended at his death and no great light shone; but who is to say what he himself saw, or who came to meet him?

For myself, I am not yet 20, and my life in this monastery stretches ahead of me. My devotion is indeed to Saint Cuthbert who healed me. But Egfroth will be an abiding memory, and much of what he told me (he who said he never taught anyone anything!) will be with me for ever. I pray that I may be as faithful in my way as he was in his.

ABOUT THE AUTHOR

Canon Kate Tristram has lived on the Holy Island of Lindisfarne since 1978 and been an ordained priest since 1994.
Before moving to the Island she was Lecturer in Religious Studies in the College of St Hild in Durham.

Kate's all-consuming hunger for breadth and depth of knowledge is ever-present. Even after retirement she was drawn back to academia and in 2000 achieved an MSc in 'Medieval Language and Text' at Edinburgh University.

She is widely recognised as an authority on medieval christianity and lectures to groups from around the world.

ABOUT THE COVER AND INTERNAL ILLUSTRATIONS

In this book, Egfroth is given charge of a cat by Saint Aidan. The cat is called Pangur. When Egfroth talked with Eadfrid as he was working on the Lindisfarne Gospels, Egfroth asks why there isn't a cat amongst all of the birds and other animals Eadfrid depicts. Eadfrid promises to include Pangur in his artwork.

For the cover Mary Fleeson has combined her illustration of Pangur with the Cat illustration from the beginning of Saint Luke's Gospel in the Lindisfarne Gospels and as there were seven 'Pangurs' over Egfroth's lifetime, she has included sketches of them throughout the book.

Mary is an artist based on Holy Island who aims to follow the great Monastic Scriptorium tradition of producing pieces of artwork that give glory to God and help His people to worship.

More information can be found about Lindisfarne Scriptorium on the Island or by visiting www.lindisfarne-scriptorium.co.uk

About St Mary's Church Holy Island.

The Holy Island of Lindisfarne is the 'cradle of Christianity in the north of England' and it resonates still with the stories and history of the 'Island Saints': St Aidan, St Oswald, St Cuthbert, and other saints, who were part of the living or telling of the story of the 'Golden Age of Northumbria'.

St Mary's Church is part of the larger monastic site founded by St Aidan, which also contains the site of the original 7th century monastery and the later 12th century Benedictine monastery, the ruins of which still stand today. St Mary's Church is understood to be one of the two Saxon twin churches, the second being where the medieval priory church presently stands. As part of a church of the Saxon monastery, it seems highly likely that St Mary's stands on the site of Aidan's original wooden church of 635.

The church is a focal point for the spiritual life of Holy Island's small community as well as welcoming many thousands of pilgrims and visitors who flock to Holy Island every year. Here they find the peace and inspiration of a special place, where 'the veil between earth and heaven is thin'. In the midst of busy lives they can bring their concerns and anxieties to God.

Part of the proceeds from the sale of this book are being donated to St Mary's as capital expenditure on the fabric of the church is beyond the community's resources and the church needs to rely on grant funding, legacies and generous donations from the Friends of St Mary's Church Holy Island scheme to pay major expenses.

If you are interested in helping support the ministry of St Mary's then please contact The Treasurer, c/o The Vicarage, Holy Island, Berwick-upon-Tweed. TD15 2RX